THE POTTERS' FIELD

THE POTTERS' FIELD

A History of the South Devon
Ball Clay Industry

L. T. C. ROLT

DAVID & CHARLES
NEWTON ABBOT   LONDON
NORTH POMFRET (VT)   VANCOUVER

ISBN 0 7153 6504 5

Set in 11 on 13pt Imprint and printed in Great
Britain by Latimer Trend & Company Ltd
Plymouth for David & Charles (Holdings)
Limited South Devon House Newton Abbot
Devon

Published in the United States of America by
David & Charles Inc North Pomfret Vermont
05053 USA

Published in Canada by Douglas David &
Charles Limited 3645 McKechnie Drive
West Vancouver BC

Contents

List of Illustrations

7

(*All photographs not otherwise acknowledged are from
the collection of Watts, Blake, Bearne*)

In Text

Foreword

As one who has always been interested in the history of the pottery industry, I have had, for many years, the ambition to place on record what is known of the history of one of its essential raw materials—ball clay—for very little information is available concerning the production of this material in the books on the history of the ceramic art.

A few years ago, I was fortunate in being able to persuade Mr R. C. F. Whiteway-Wilkinson, whose family for many generations has been associated with ball clay and its production, to delve into the past and assemble what information was still available. This having been done, I was equally fortunate in securing Mr L. T. C. Rolt's agreement to turn this information into an account of the history of the industry and associated activities, which we now present to all those who are interested in the industry's past.

It is suggested that although we look forward to many more years of ball clay production, the present decade will witness dramatic changes in many of the ways the industry has functioned.

The production of ball clay in the traditional sense has been brought to a high standard of mechanical efficiency, as is evidenced by the Queen's Award for Technology in 1969. In spite of this, the next decade will see the beginning of revolutionary changes in the whole concept of the production process.

The completion of the motorway system, giving a direct link from Stoke-on-Trent to Exeter, and its extension by 1975–6 as a dual carriageway through the Bovey basin; and the anticipated implementation of the Teignmouth Harbour Improvement Scheme during the same period, are improvements of outstanding importance in the method of distribution of the clays produced.

In the sphere of industrial relations, the change from piecework

9

and its associated methods of payment, to a secure weekly salary, and the greater involvement of all employees in the industry's affairs, heralds a new type of relationship between employer and employee.

The completion of the concentration of the industry to two principal companies has established a firm financial foundation upon which to build the technological development of the future.

It is also pleasant to record that the industry has come to recognise and accept its responsibility to future generations for the conservation of its resources and the restoration of amenity, as is evidenced by the Countryside Award in 1970. Exhausted clay workings will no longer be abandoned; their afteruse will be properly planned.

Because of all these changes, I feel sure that we are at the most important turning point in the industry's long history. This is surely the best time to recall the past as we take a new road into the future.

C. D. Pike

Introduction

ABOUT twelve years ago I spent a brief winter holiday at Teignmouth. It was my first visit to a town which I had previously thought of only as a holiday resort having no indigenous, workaday life of its own apart from its rows of seaside boarding-houses and hotels. Imagine then my surprise and curiosity when I discovered that Teignmouth possessed a harbour and an extremely active one at that. Hardly a high tide passed without at least one small grey coaster either entering or, deep-laden, leaving the harbour by the narrow channel between Den Point and the red sandstone headland called the Ness. What was the reason for all this activity? What were these little ships carrying? 'South Devon ball clay', I was told in a tone of voice which expressed such astonishment at my ignorance that I confess I was too cowardly to betray it still further by asking what precisely this substance was, how it was obtained and for what purpose it was used. I supposed ball clay to be due to some strange geological freak, and visualised that somewhere in the mysterious heart of Devon there must be men who, for purposes unknown, dug up clay that had been transformed by some unimaginable freak of nature into large nuggets about the size of cricket balls.

In this state of innocence I remained until the late autumn of 1971 when I was asked if I would write a history of the South Devon ball clay industry by its largest producer, Watts, Blake, Bearne & Co Ltd of Newton Abbot. I was thereupon initiated into the mysteries of a trade of which I knew nothing, and very fascinating I found them. The chapters which follow are the product of this enlightenment.

The history of the Watts, Blake, Bearne partnership goes back over a hundred years, but the history of the industry in which the firm has played so conspicuous a part goes back much further than this—to the last decades of the seventeenth century, in fact. Practically nothing had been written about the history of the industry or about its past or present practices. So for a complete ignoramus such as I to have gathered enough historical material and an understanding of how the industry ticked sufficiently adequate to enable this book to be written would have been impossible short of going to live in the area. Very fortunately for me, however, a great deal of this spadework had already been done by Mr R. C. F. Whiteway-Wilkinson and embodied in a typescript which was made available to me and proved absolutely invaluable. In this way he could be said to have acted as my research assistant, despite the fact that we were unknown to each other at the time he was doing his work. I could not have wished for a more able collaborator. For, as the following pages make clear, Mr Whiteway-Wilkinson was born with ball clay in his veins, if I may be forgiven for using such an uncomfortable phrase. Long familiarity with the industry and its locale enabled him to seek out the most likely sources of historical information and to understand the significance of what he found. His quest took him to the Newton Abbot Library, the Exeter City Library and Muniment Room, the Devonshire County Record Office, the Clifford Estate Papers at Ugbrooke, the Earl of Devon's Estate Papers in the archives at County Hall, the Watts Estate Papers and the offices of Newton Abbot RDC, Chudleigh Parish Council, the *Mid Devon Advertiser*, English China Clays Ltd, the Teignmouth Quay Co Ltd, and Messrs Tozers, Solicitors, Newton Abbot. He was also fortunate in being able to tap the phenomenal memory of Mr W. J. V. Watts, past chairman and president of Watts, Blake, Bearne & Co Ltd until his death in April 1972 in his ninety-first year. This book owes a very great deal, not only to Mr Whiteway-Wilkinson but to all those individuals who so willingly granted him access to original material and helped him in many other ways.

For my part, I am immensely grateful to Mr Whiteway-Wilkinson for so cheerfully making available to me the fruits of his labour. Most of the facts in this history were drawn from his typescript. For the rest, I am indebted to two sources: the authors of the works listed in my Bibliography and, last but not least the directors and staff of Watts, Blake, Bearne & Co Ltd for their patient helpfulness under my inquisition. In particular, I would like to acknowledge the help of the chairman and managing director, Mr C. D. Pike. It is to his enthusiasm and to his interest in the past, present and future of the ball clay industry that this book owes its existence.

L.T.C.R.

CHAPTER ONE

Ball Clay and Its Uses

IN most pottery and china, in sanitary ware, refractories and electrical insulators ball clay is an essential ingredient. Yet to almost anyone outside these industries the term 'ball clay' is meaningless. On the other hand, everyone has heard of china clay because the name is self-explanatory. By contrast, the term ball clay is obscure to the layman because it originated in the method by which it was first extracted by cutting it out with a spade in a series of cubical lumps which were referred to in Devon as 'balls'.

Ball clay and china clay consist mainly of the same basic ingredient—kaolinite which was formed by a natural chemical process occurring in remote geological time. The effect of superheated steam and hot acid gases, containing compounds of boron and fluorine, issuing from the hot interior of the earth through fissures in its granite crust, was to decompose the felspars in the granite to form kaolinite. This process of decomposition, which is known as hydrothermal alteration, occurred fairly commonly in the granite spine of the western peninsular that extends from west Devon to the tip of Cornwall. Wherever it has occurred the granite has been transformed into a white, powdery substance or, where decomposition has been only partial, into the comparatively soft white rock known as china stone or petuntse.*

The difference between ball clay and china clay is that the former was washed out of the parent granite by the natural action of rivers and streams and subsequently deposited elsewhere by sedimentation, whereas the latter remains in situ. This means that in its natural state as found, china clay is not a clay at all in the strict meaning of the word which derives from the Anglo-Saxon *Claeg*,

* Also called Moorstone or Growan Stone in the West Country.

meaning sticky. It is only after it has been washed out of the parent
rock by the action of high-pressure water jets, and the resulting
white slurry has been induced to solidify, that it begins to acquire
some of the characteristics of clay. In other words, china clay is
made by simulating the natural process by which ball clay was
formed. However, as we shall see presently, in the course of this
natural process, ball clay acquired certain valuable properties
which are lacking in china clay.

Paradoxically, although ball clay is comparatively little known, it
was being dug in South Devon, and its unique value was partially
appreciated, at least fifty years before the discovery of the great
china clay deposits of Cornwall. The man responsible for that
discovery, which had an influence upon the development of the ball
clay trade, was William Cookworthy (1705–80), a Quaker of
Kingsbridge in Devon.

The terms kaolin or kaolinite and petuntse are of Chinese deriva-
tion. They commemorate the fact that the making of translucent
china or porcelain was an art discovered and developed in China
centuries before the secret was known in Europe. Europeans could
only marvel at the delicate quality and refinement of Chinese porcelain compared with their own coarse and crude earthenware. In
England it was Cookworthy who at last discovered both the recipe
for what became known as hard-paste porcelain and the ingredients
in Cornwall from which to make it. He patented the process in 1768
and, in the same year, set up a factory in Plymouth in which to
practice the art. Unfortunately for him, however, he soon discovered
that the recipe was only half the secret; the other half lay in the
cooking or 'firing'. In this he ran into technical difficulties so intractable that after only two years the Plymouth works closed down.
Cookworthy seems to have lost heart at this juncture. for it was on
the initiative of one of his partners, Richard Champion, that a
second porcelain manufactory was established in Bristol.

This Bristol enterprise proved more successful than its predecessor. In 1774, when Cookworthy assigned his patent rights to

Page 17　(above) *Binny Quarry in 1949, a typical open clay working which has now been reclaimed for agriculture;* (below) *two views of a modern drilling rig used to prove clay resources in the Bovey basin*

Page 18   *Primitive and modern methods of clay shredding*

Champion, the latter promptly petitioned Parliament for a fourteen-year extension of the patent which would have given him an exclusive right to the manufacture of translucent porcelain. This petition was bitterly opposed by the potters of Staffordshire led by Josiah Wedgwood and a long and costly legal battle ensued. Despite the fact that the Cookworthy/Champion process was still far from perfect, the Staffordshire men saw in the patent a barrier to progress because it protected the use of china clay and china stone. The settlement eventually arrived at was that, while Champion retained the exclusive right to manufacture porcelain by Cookworthy's process, the other potters might use china clay and stone in the manufacture of their wares.

The activity of Cookworthy and Champion undoubtedly provoked a competitive spirit among the Staffordshire potters. It provided a stimulus to improve the quality of their products which influenced the demand for ball clay. As we shall see presently, there was another and earlier competitive stimulus at work in the shape of the productions of the Dutch potters.

The particle size of china clay is comparatively coarse which has the effect of limiting its plasticity. If a 'body' were to be made entirely from china clay it would be 'short' like pastry and impossible to manipulate. And even if it were possible for a potter to 'throw' a vase of china clay upon his wheel, the result would be so deficient in what he would call 'green strength' that it would be impossible to handle or to load into his kiln without it falling to pieces. It was this unfortunate characteristic of china clay which was no doubt the cause of many of the early difficulties of Cookworthy and Champion.

As a result of the natural process that led to its creation, ball clay possesses virtues which china clay lacks. In the course of its river journey it had lost most of the coarse quartz and other granite residues by the time it was deposited. At the same time it had picked up certain organic particles derived from humus, plant debris and the like which are wholly lacking in china clay. Although the

B

particle size of ball clay varies according to quality, it is generally finer than that of china clay and it is this characteristic that gives ball clay its high plasticity and 'green' or unfired strength that makes it so valuable to the potter. The higher the proportion of 'fines' in the clay, the greater its green strength. Particles of organic matter in the clay also contribute to its strength, and as such particles tend to darken the natural colour of the clay when found, the so-called black ball clays (actually a very dark brown) are the strongest clays of all. To these organic particles other very useful characteristics of certain of the finer ball clays are attributed: their fluidity when used as a liquid slip and their thixotropy, which means the tendency of such a slip to thicken. Both these attributes are of particular value where pottery articles are produced by casting into moulds instead of by the immemorial process of 'throwing' on the potter's wheel.

Despite what has been said in the preceding paragraph, certain grades of ball clay still contain quite a high proportion of free silica, that is to say comparatively large particles of quartz. These are usually referred to as stoneware clays because their principal use in the formative years of the pottery industry was in the production of stoneware,* high quality vitrified domestic tableware. They were also used for domestic cooking utensils and later for the production of technical ceramics. These siliceous ball clays usually contain a proportion of other impurities including iron oxide and for this reason their 'body' colour is buff or pale yellow when fired. For the purposes for which they are used, however, this body colour is of no consequence. By contrast, the clays containing only combined silica in minute particles, such as the black ball clay already mentioned, produce a fired body that is either white or the palest ivory colour. This is a characteristic of the greatest importance and its discovery was of immense value to the pottery industry.

Ball clay deposits are sometimes found at considerable depth.

---

* Stoneware is simply a harder form of ware produced by firing at a higher temperature with the effect that the clay is partially vitrified.

They occur in seams of varying breadth and quality separated by bands of lignite, an imperfectly formed brown coal in which the texture of the original woody material may often be recognised. The finer silica-free clays contain carbonaceous material in varying quantity and their colour when found may be black, brown or varying shades of blue, but they share the common characteristic that when fired they produce a body that is either white or a pale cream.

These ball clay beds were laid down in the Tertiary Period (late Oligocene and early Miocene) approximately 25 to 30 million years ago when England was joined to the European land mass. The reason why, throughout the world, ball clay is a comparatively rare mineral is that, in most cases, it was swept by the rivers out to sea. It was only where natural topography originally allowed such rivers to form fairly large lakes and so slow down their rate of flow that the kaolinite clays were trapped and deposited inland. England is fortunate in possessing the finest ball clays in the world, but these are only to be found in the vicinity of Poole and Wareham in Dorset, in North Devon within the parishes of Meeth and Peters Marland, near Torrington, and in South Devon between Bovey Tracey and Newton Abbot. It is thought that in the remote past a powerful river flowed eastward out of Dartmoor which would account for the Dorset clay beds which are believed to be the oldest by some millions of years. It is also conjectured that until some much more recent date in geological time the river Dart still flowed eastward to join the predecessor of the river Bovey in the lower part of the Bovey basin near Newton Abbot. The recent discovery of alluvial tin in the gravel that overlies the clay deposits hereabouts would seem to support this theory because there are no known veins of tin in the immediate locality.

Clays from these three English sources differ appreciably from each other when fired. Certain South Devon grades fire the whitest ('off white to creamy white'), North Devon clay is described as 'pale ivory to ivory' and Dorset as 'ivory, buff or red'. Vitrification

STRUCTURAL SETTING OF THE BOVEY BASIN

HALDON

R. TEIGN

DARTMOOR

PALAEOZOIC ROCKS

Structural Setting of the Bovey basin

in firing depends upon the amount of fluxing oxides present in the clay and this also varies regionally. The Dorset clays and some of those from South Devon vitrify appreciably at temperatures of 1,100° C and above, where North Devon clays and the remainder of those from South Devon do not begin to vitrify until a temperature of 1,200° C is reached.

In Dorset the blue clays are the best and the whole bed covers the largest area although much of the deposit is siliceous and shallow. The Bovey basin with which we are here concerned is the richest deposit of the three; its output has been consistently greater over the years and it probably possesses the greatest reserves. It consists of an area of about 12 square miles extending north-west from Newton Abbot and a second, smaller area 2 miles in diameter immediately to the south of that town. The whole was once a lake, the bottom of which slowly subsided, possibly under the weight of successive depositions of clay and lignite, the latter formed from waterlogged 'rafts' of floating timber, mainly Sequoia, Nyssa and Cinnamon. Consequently, although the surface area of the Bovey basin is smaller than that of the so-called Bagshot Beds in Dorset, its depth is much greater. A famous borehole at Teigngrace near the centre of the basin proved in 1918 the existence of seams of clay at a depth of nearly 700ft. A still deeper borehole made in 1972 extended this knowledge to still greater depths, although to date 600ft is the maximum depth from which clay has been extracted. The profile of

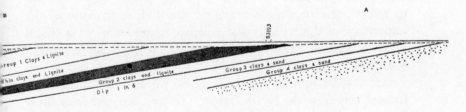

Cross-section of clay seams

the seams is bowl-shaped in section, the seams outcropping through
the overburden of alluvial gravel and sand on the east and west and
dipping steeply towards the centre of the present valley where the
river Teign and its tributary the Bovey now flow.

It was along the eastern outcrop that clay of good quality was first
found and dug, stoneware and white-firing clays outcropping in
parallel, and to this day it is in the vicinity of this outcrop from
Newton Abbot by Kingsteignton and Chudleigh Knighton to
Knighton Heath and Bradley, a little to the south-east of Bovey
Tracey, that the principal clay workings are to be found. The clays
of the western outcrop were less readily accessible and of poorer
quality and were therefore not exploited in the early days when clay
could only be got from shallow open pits. Today, however, clay of
fine quality is obtained by underground mining at Sandford Orleigh
and at other points to the west of the river Teign.

The Romans are said to have been the first to discover and exploit the Devon clay, but after the Romans left Britain the beds lay
undisturbed until the beginning of the seventeenth century.
According to tradition, it was at Cornwood in South Devon in 1564
that Sir Walter Raleigh smoked his first pipe of tobacco, and it was
after this that—sporadically at first—Devon clay began to be dug
for pipe making. For this reason it became known as Pipe Clay or
Cutty Clay. As the tobacco habit spread throughout the country, so
pipe making became a flourishing craft in most of the larger pro-
vincial cities and towns and it was to supply this new industry
that small quantities of Devon pipe-clay began to be shipped
to many ports round the coasts of England. A measure of the
importance of this trade is that a clause in an Act of 1662 (Carol
II, C 18, Section VIII) forbade the export of pipe-clay to foreign
countries.

One noted centre for pipe making was Chester, and small quantities of clay from the North Devon beds were shipped from Bideford to the Port of Chester as early as 1691. By 1730, these annual
shipments to Chester, though still relatively small, had trebled in

volume. From this it is reasonable to infer that the potters of neighbouring North Staffordshire had discovered the merits of the white-firing Devon clay and were using it in small quantities in the form of a liquid slip to decorate their native brown earthenware.

In the early 1680s, a Dutch potter named John Arieno Van Hamme settled in England and was granted a patent to make 'tiles, Porcelaine and other Earthen Wares, after the way practised in Holland, which hath not been practised in this our Kingdom'. Again, in 1688, when the Prince of Orange, 'Dutch William', claimed the English throne, among his retinue he is said to have brought with him those noted potters, the Elers brothers. In this way the making of Dutch Delft ware was introduced to England. The contrast between the white Delft ware and the crude brown earthenware of Staffordshire was so striking as to create considerable alarm and despondency among the Staffordshire potters and there is an improbable tradition that two of them, Astbury and Twyford, feigned idiocy in order to obtain employment with the Elers brothers and so learn their secrets.

Although early Dutch Delft ware was crude, it was a decided improvement upon brown earthenware and it started a fashion for 'white ware'. The latter's origin is still perpetuated in Ireland where, among the older generation, all white ware is still referred to as Delft. The whiteness of the original Dutch Delft was achieved by covering the biscuit body of red or brown earthenware with a thick galena (lead) glaze rendered white and opaque by mixing it with tin oxide. This white glaze was decorated with designs in blue. Such a method of concealing a dark body colour beneath a white glaze could never be entirely satisfactory due to inevitable variations in the thickness of the liquid glaze in which it was dipped. Hence the Staffordshire potters applied themselves to the task of improving upon their Dutch competitors' wares by evolving a body which would fire white, or near white and so would not betray inequalities in the glazing. Consequently it was at this period in history that the white-firing clays of Devon and Dorset came into their own. In this connection it is interesting to note that the famous Delft pottery De Porceleyne Fles has used both Devon ball clays and china clays in its body composition for the past hundred years. The wheel has thus turned full circle.

The pioneer developer of what became known as 'cream ware' in Staffordshire was John Astbury of Shelton (1688–1743). Whether he used Devon clay for this purpose is doubtful, though Shaw* specifically states that he achieved a cream-coloured body by mixing Devonshire clay with calcined and ground flint (silica). However, other authorities hold that Astbury used flint in conjunction with local clays which, despite careful selection, fired to a deep cream colour due to their contamination by iron oxides. At this time, ware was fired only once, that is to say it was glazed in the green state. Enoch Booth of Tunstall was the pioneer of 'twice firing'. Booth fired his ware in the unglazed state (biscuit firing), then dipped it in a suspended solution of lead ore, ground flint and pipe-clay, dusted it with colouring oxides, and fired it again (glost firing). It is a fault of the finest white-firing ball clays that their wet-to-fired shrinkage is high. In the early bodies, which were extremely high in ball clay, this was a fatal defect which inhibited their use because of cracking and for this reason they became known to potters as 'cracking clays'. However, the virtues of the finest white-firing ball clays could be utilised and this disadvantage minimised by their judicious mixing with another type of clay and with other ingredients to produce a vastly improved pottery 'body'. This was the achievement of Josiah Wedgwood.

Whether Astbury used Devon clay or not is an open question, but it is certain that Thomas Whieldon began to do so sometime after 1740 when he opened a small pottery at Fenton Low. It is significant that the greatest of Staffordshire potters, Josiah Wedgwood, was in partnership with Whieldon at Fenton Low from 1754 to

---

* Simeon Shaw (c1784–1859). His *History of Staffordshire* (1829) is considered unreliable and inaccurate but includes much information not to be found elsewhere.

1759. Wedgwood had a lifetime's experience of the pottery trade having, at the age of eleven, started as an apprentice in his elder brother Thomas's Churchyard Works at Burslem. It was after he had severed his connection with Whieldon and started a pottery on his own account at Burslem in May 1759 that he embarked on a long and tireless series of experiments with clays and glazes which led to his spectacular successes.

One of the difficulties that Wedgwood set himself to overcome was that, owing to the presence of impurities in the clays then used, the colour of the cream wares produced was inconstant and unpredictable and such variations led to understandable dissatisfaction on the part of retailers and customers when they ordered replacements. Another source of difficulty was the cracking or 'crazing' of glazes in the kiln due to body shrinkage or, conversely, expansion under heat. Wedgwood patiently overcame these snags until, in 1762, he triumphantly presented a caudle and breakfast set of his newly perfected white-bodied Staffordshire ware to Queen Charlotte. So far as the pottery industry was concerned, this was a master-stroke of publicity. Soon after, many potteries, not only in Staffordshire but elsewhere, were marketing their own versions of white-bodied ware under the generic name of 'Queen's Ware'. In 1777, Wedgwood crowned his success by making a magnificent Imperial Russian service for Catherine II. This consisted of 952 pieces hand-painted with over a thousand different scenes and it cost the empress £3,500.

The success of Wedgwood's 'Queen's Ware' and its many counterparts by other hands, such as those produced by David Dunderdale at Leeds and later at Castleford, ensured a large and expanding market for Devon clays. Instead of pipe-clay, it now became known as potter's clay. We know that Wedgwood was using South Devon ball clay at this period because, in a letter dated 13 March 1771 from Etruria to his partner Thomas Bentley in London, urging Bentley to obtain for him a supply of Dorset clay, he writes: 'To enable Mr. Rhodes to judge better of the sort, I will send a sample of Poole Clay and another of Teignmouth Clay, that we may avoid buying the latter as we have enough of it here.'*

The Staffordshire potters countered the threat of competition from Cookworthy's hard-paste porcelain in two ways; by improving the quality of their own white-ware and by developing a soft-paste porcelain in which ground flint and calcined bones were added to the body. This translucent ware became known as bone china.† Yet even this bone china included a substantial proportion of ball clay in addition to china clay in the body to make good the deficiencies of the latter. Ball clay was needed to provide the necessary plasticity and 'green strength' to enable the unfired ware to be handled in the pottery and stacked in the kiln for firing. For the same reason, all Wedgwood's famous blue ware, his black basalt and green jasper, contained a proportion of Devon ball clay.

When the potteries of Staffordshire and the north became dependent on clay from the West Country to the exclusion of the local product it may be wondered why the industry did not migrate and re-establish itself nearer to its source of raw material. The answer is that so long as the industry fired its wares in coal-fired kilns, or 'bottle ovens' as they were called, it consumed such quantities of coal that it had to be sited near the coalfields. In other words it was easier and cheaper to transport clay to Staffordshire than it was to carry the necessary coal to Cornwall or Devon. For this reason, although potteries were established in Devon, at Bovey Tracey,‡

---

* From typescript copy of original letter kindly furnished by the Wedgwood Museum.

† In 1780, Champion disposed of Cookworthy's patent for hard-paste porcelain to a syndicate of Staffordshire potters who began manufacturing it at a pottery in Tunstall and, later, at New Hall, Shelton. Competition from bone china was such that this venture ceased production in 1810.

‡ From 1766 onwards contemporary accounts of this pottery agree that repeated attempts were made to overcome the fuel problem by burning the local lignite but all failed because a sufficiently high temperature could not be attained.

Wedgwood visited the Bovey pottery in the course of a journey from London to Cornwall in May 1775 and expressed his contempt for the pottery and its products in his Diary: 'A Mr. Crisp of London endeavoured to make a kind of porcelain here, but did little more than make some experiments, and those unsuccessful ones. They afterwards made white stone ware glazed with Salts, and had a fireman, and I believe some other workmen from our country, but it was still a losing concern to and in Dorset, they never rivalled Staffordshire.* There was another reason, too, and that was the unique expertise developed over the years by Staffordshire pottery workers of every grade. That is why to this day the industry remains centred on the famous Five Towns even though, since the introduction of the continuous tunnel kilns heated by gas or electricity, it has long ceased to be directly dependent on coal.

In the sustained effort to improve the quality of their wares, the potters learned, by trial and error and at the cost of many a spoiled firing, a great deal about the properties and behaviour of different clays. They became the first clay technologists and they kept their knowledge to themselves. The ingredients and proportions of each potter's 'body' were his jealously guarded secrets and in this new technology the West Country clay producers at first played only a very minor role. It was their job to supply the clay to the requirements of the potter's agent and not to reason why. Their own testing procedure was confined to biting the clay. If it gritted against the teeth it contained free silica and was therefore a stoneware clay. The latter-day history of the ball clay industry has been marked by the gradual transfer of technological know-how from the consumer to the producer. Today, the customer, whether he be a potter or any other of the many industrial consumers of ball clay, demands from the clay producer a product of predictable behaviour which has been tailored to his particular need. It may be a clay from a particular

them. It is now under the management of one Ellis, and the money advanced from some persons at a distance. They now make Queens Ware, or cream-colour, but it is a poor trifling concern and conducted in a wretched slovenly manner.' He goes on to write of the local clay, of flints from Halldown [now Haldon] hill, near Exeter and coals 'only 2/6 per ton, at the pit, and so near the works, that only wheelbarrows are used for their conveyance to the works'. He then concludes: 'Notwithstanding all which advantages, besides labour being much cheaper with them than us, we can carry their flints from Devonshire into Staffordshire, there manufacture them into ware, and send it back to their own doors, better and cheaper than they can make it!'—Wedgwood Society, *Proceedings*, Vol I, No 1 and 2.

* There was an exact historical parallel to this further west in the failure of local attempts to smelt Cornish copper. They could not compete with Welsh smelters who had ready access to coal.

seam or, more likely, it will be a mixture of several clays precisely blended to produce the desired characteristics.

For many years the Devon clays were supplied in the lump or ball exactly as extracted. In the earliest period the bulk of the clay dug was of the stoneware variety and, when taken from the pit, it was conveyed to long, low storage buildings having massive stone walls to resist the weight of the piled clay. These were known locally as clay cellars. On the other hand, the finer non-siliceous white-firing clays demanded by the makers of white or Queen's ware were stored in open 'bedplaces' to be weathered by exposure to sun, rain and frost. Potters then considered that such a weathering process was essential in order to homogenise the clay so that it would work well, and some of the older potters insisted that the lumps supplied to them should have been weathered for at least two years. A proportion of the clay dug was found to be 'short', that is to say it would not cohere in lumps but broke into small pieces on extraction. It was also stained—usually by the presence of iron and often contained large grains of sand or quartz. Clay of this character was known as 'brokes' and commanded a lower price because it was generally found to have a bad colour when fired.

In 1938, one South Devon clay company received an order from America for potter's clay to be supplied in 'shredded' form, that is to say the clay lumps were to be cut into small pieces about an inch long and subsequently stored under cover to reduce the moisture content and therefore its weight and freight cost. To meet this novel request, the lumps of clay as dug were cut by means of an adapted turnip cutter and a previously open bedplace was roofed over as a store for the shredded clay. This was to prove a turning point in the history of the industry, for today only a minute fraction of the total output of clay is supplied in the lump or weathered form. For obvious reasons shredded clay is easier and cheaper to handle mechanically and to transport. It also facilitates both the blending of different clays and further processing such as milling and calcining. Using modern homogenising methods, it has been found that the old process of natural weathering is unnecessary.

The modern clay works is distinguished by its large covered storage sheds where, in many separate bays, the different types of clay are stored first in lump and then in shredded form in huge heaps. Here the clay brought from open pits or mines by dumpers or tipping trucks is fed into the hoppers of specially developed shredding machines which, after cutting the clay, eject it on to the heap by means of a short, fast-moving conveyor belt. This type of machine is built by the local Newton Abbot engineering firm of H. Beare & Sons Ltd. The shredder is mounted on rubber-tyred wheels because mobility is a great advantage in enabling a machine to move from one storage bay to another, particularly when the mixing of clays of different grades is carried out in the storage sheds.

In the construction of modern clay storage sheds the greatest care is taken to obviate any risk of the product being contaminated. All structural steelwork is galvanised and an infilling of timber is used to prevent any possibility of rust particles falling on to the clay. Such particles would cause black spots to appear on the fired ceramic.

Although the first shredded clay was produced in 1938, the effect of World War II on the ball clay industry was disastrous owing to the shortage of manpower and the contraction of the market. Conquently it remained a backward industry until after the war and it is since 1946 that the whole industry has been transformed by a remarkable revolution in the techniques of clay getting and clay processing which has not only very greatly improved the quality and variety of the product but made possible a prodigious increase in annual output. Successive mergers of clay-producing firms make comparative output figures misleading, but an increase in the annual output per man from 368 tons in 1951 to 974 tons in 1970 gives a fair picture of what has been achieved. Much of the credit for this spectacularly rapid revolution in methods is due to the industry's engineers who have combed Europe for the most suitable plant for their purpose and, in many cases, skilfully adapted and developed it to serve their particular needs.

The first small plant for drying and pulverising clay was installed in South Devon in 1922 and although it was unsatisfactory, small quantities of pulverised clay continued to be supplied from that date forward. In 1947 a new type of pulverising plant was developed, using an Attritor designed by Alfred Herbert for pulverising coal. This machine proved so satisfactory for its new purpose that successively larger models were introduced during the 1950s. Unfortunately the method of drying the clay with coke fuel was unsatisfactory. It was very laborious and the fly ash produced was prone to contaminate the clay. This problem was solved by the end of the decade when the plant was converted to oil firing using the Toroidal burner. In today's pulverising plant, which is automatic, the clay is dried and pulverised simultaneously by a continuous process before being delivered into paper bags which are compressed and palletised for easy loading on to road vehicles by fork lift trucks.

The calcining of ball clay consists of heating it in a rotary kiln, a process which converts it into 'Chamotte', a product which is less reactive and so reduces firing time of the ceramic in which it is used. It is used chiefly in the manufacture of modern refractories. Once again, the process took some years to perfect. Experiments began in 1961, but 'Chamotte' did not come into full production until 1966. This was due to the tendency of the clay particles to agglomerate at high temperatures in the calcining kiln until it was no longer possible to maintain the correct atmosphere and the operation had to close down. This trouble, which was termed 'balling' or 'ringing' was eventually overcome in three ways: by eliminating 'fines' from the clay, by using a lighter oil fuel to fire the kiln and by introducing closed circuit television to enable the operator to see what was happening inside the kiln and control the speed of the process accordingly. Natural gas is also now used in place of oil fuel in the pulverising process.

Although still referred to by its traditional title of the ball clay industry, in fact today only 5 per cent of the industry's output is supplied in the lump. Shredded and blended clays account for at least three-quarters of the total, the remainder being accounted for by various dried and pulverised forms. The latter include clays that have been chemically treated to make them free-flowing. This type of clay is supplied to the fertiliser industry where it is used to prevent artificial fertilisers caking in storage. Clay is also used in the manufacture of pesticides and in the iron and steel industry; it is also extensively employed as a filler in the manufacture of rubber and adhesives. Yet despite an expanding range of new applications in the modern world, the largest consumers of ball clays are still the makers of ceramics and refractories.

An ancient industry, especially an extractive one, usually evolves a language and nomenclature of its own that can be bewildering to the layman. The South Devon ball clays were distinguished by names, some referring to colour when found and some to colour when fired, others to the particular purpose for which they were used or to particular physical characteristics. Here are some examples:

Cutty Clay Clay suitable for the manufacture of clay pipes. As this was the oldest recorded use of South Devon clay, the term then appears to have been applied to any variety of clay from the Bovey basin or from North Devon.

Household Clay A non-plastic white clay used for whitening doorsteps or flagstones.

Plastic Pinks/Short Pinks Two varieties of stoneware clays of differing plasticity but of a pink colour when found.

Ivory Ball Clay A potter's clay firing to an ivory colour.

China Ball Clay A light coloured, white-firing potter's clay, highly aluminous and sometimes referred to as 'Alum'.

Light, Brown, Blue or Black Pottery Clay Four white-firing potter's clays distinguished by their differing colours when found.

Mottled Clay   A stoneware clay of variegated colour when found, sometimes called 'Glady'.

Stilt Clay   A vitreous stoneware clay which was especially suitable for making 'Stilts'—the three-legged separators used to prevent plates or other pieces of pottery from sticking together when fired in the kiln.

Saggar Clay   A crude variety of refractory clay used for making the 'saggars' in which pottery is placed in the green state before biscuit firing.

Top or Coarse Top   A stoneware clay used with an admixture of other clays.

Figgy Clay   Clay with a nodular or roughened appearance. The nodules consist of lignite.

Hawse Clay   A clay which crumbles when found, yet becomes plastic when worked up. Most of the deeper seams of white-firing clays of the best quality could be so described. Sometimes called 'auze' or 'auzey' clay by the older miners.

These bewildering definitions which have grown up over many years have now given place to a less romantic but altogether simpler, more rational and less confusing method of classification. One of the most important results of the scientific study of clays by the producers with the aid of modern laboratory equipment has been the discovery that the ball clays of the Bovey basin could be classified into four distinctive groups according to their behaviour and characteristics. This exact knowledge enables the producer to recommend a clay which will best suit the particular purpose for which it is required. This may be a natural clay falling within one or other of the four groups or, much more likely, a blend of clays from more than one group. Moreover, such blends of clay make possible the fullest use of modern methods of open pit working where it is often impossible economically to mine clay of one group only. These four groups are:

Page 35 (above) *Modern plant for bagging powdered clay;* (below) *modern clay research laboratories at Park House, Newton Abbot*

Page 36   (above) *Cutting clay 'balls' by hand, c1920;* (below) *a typical early timbered square pit*

No 1: The Extra White Firing Clays   These include the finest quality of potter's clays. They remain exceptionally white at temperatures exceeding 1,200° C, a characteristic that is mainly due to the fact that they contain little ferrous oxide or titanium dioxide and to a lesser extent to the presence of varying amounts of carbonaceous matter from 0·2 per cent to 4·0 per cent. The more carbonaceous clays in this group are brown or almost black in the natural state and have a finer particle size than those low in carbon. Their thermal expansion characteristics are quite different from those of clays in the other three groups, resembling more closely those of china clay. They are the most refractory ball clays to be found in this country, having an exceptionally high alumina content.

No 2: The Dark Blue Clays   These clays fire white up to 1,000° C and off-white above this temperature. They are mainly carbonaceous, and exceptionally fine grained, but because their silica and mica content is greater they have a higher peak expansion than the clays in Group 1. These are the strongest clays in the South Devon field, tough, plastic, and having exceptional bonding power. These qualities make them particularly valuable in the making of earthenware by automatic machinery and, because they have excellent casting properties combined with high green strength, to the maker of sanitary ware also.

No 3: The Light Blue Ball Clays   These contain no carbon but a higher proportion of quartz than the clays of the first two groups and this gives them a higher expansion rate up to 600° C. However, the absence of carbon makes them suitable for rapid firing. Though very plastic, they do not possess the high green strength of the Group 2 clays although they are more thixotropic in character. This last quality is particularly valuable in the liquid slips used by the makers of cast sanitary ware and consequently for this purpose they are frequently blended with the clays of other groups. Because their content of ferric oxide and titanium dioxide is higher than those in Groups 1 and 2, they fire to an off-white or ivory colour at temperatures over 1,000° C.

c

No 4: The Siliceous Ball Clays   These used to be called the stoneware clays. They all contain at least 30 per cent of free quartz and this accounts from their high expansion rate. They are of much coarser grain than the clays of the other three groups and because their proportion of ferric oxide and titanium dioxide is the highest, they fire off-white at temperatures below 1,100° C and to a buff colour above. The clays in this group are used in stoneware bodies and as refractory bonding clays.

From this brief description of the clays of the four groups it will be seen how each combines some particularly valuable property with other characteristics which are not so desirable. From this it is easy to understand how, by a judicious blending of clays from different groups, the particular virtues of each may be combined in one clay mix which will then possess all the required characteristics for a particular purpose. This was an operation which was once performed by the master potter when he mixed his 'body' from various clays in a liquid state. In this the potter was guided by his long experience of the behaviour of different clays in his kiln. This same blending operation which was once performed by the potter empirically is now carried out scientifically by the clay producer with the clay in the shredded state in the storage shed, guided by exact information supplied by his laboratory.

A ceramic 'body' includes other ingredients besides ball clay. Nevertheless, the day may not be far off when the clay producer will offer to the pottery manufacturer a range of standard 'bodies' designed to suit the particular requirements of the industry. Already things have moved a long way from the days when the potter guarded his 'body' formula as jealously as an alchemist, while the clay producer was looked upon as an ignoramus whose only method of testing the properties of clay was to bite it.

CHAPTER TWO

Clay Traders, Merchants and Companies

THE principal owners of clay-bearing lands in the Bovey basin in the eighteenth and nineteenth centuries were the Lords Clifford of Ugbrooke, the Earls of Devon (the Courtenay Estate), the Dukes of Somerset, the Ecclesiastical Commissioners and, for a period, the Templers of Stover House, a family responsible for developing the Haytor Granite Quarries and constructing both the Haytor Granite Tramway and the Stover canal which was to play an important part in the story of the South Devon ball clay trade. The Stover Estate, together with the tramway and canal were sold to the Duke of Somerset in 1829.

The first people to exploit the local clay deposits were most probably tenant farmers on these estates who were lucky enough to find clay on their lands and to have the wit to exploit it. Almost certainly the first clay to be dug went to local pipe-makers. The first recorded shipment of clay out of South Devon occurs in 1700 when a certain John Osland shipped '20 tons of Tobacco Pipe Clay' from Teignmouth to London. Similar consignments had been sent to Plymouth by sea as early as 1694. Apparently these early ventures were not a success, probably because the local producers lacked merchandising experience and connections. The first successful clay merchant in the area was a Dorset man, William Crawford of Poole, who leased clay land in the Bovey basin and exported 490 tons to London from Teignmouth in 1726-9. Thereafter the tonnage shipped was small but regular until 1742 when it began steadily to increase. London at first claimed the bulk of the shipments, but how much of this was used by pipe-makers and how much by potters there is no means of knowing. It is fair to assume that a proportion went to the London pottery trade which had been stimu-

39

lated by Dutch influence. The Staffordshire potters, however, did not allow this state of affairs to exist for very long. The first small shipment of South Devon clay to Staffordshire via the Port of Liverpool was made in August, 1729, yet by 1758 Liverpool's share of the total shipments amounted to 56 per cent as compared with London's 31 per cent. Seven years later, in 1765, Liverpool's annual imports of clay had doubled to 2,163 tons. These figures reflect the successful efforts the Staffordshire potters were making to surpass their London rivals and also a growing activity in the Bovey basin.

Writing between 1747 and 1762, Dean Milles* describes the local clay-getting activity thus:

> *Kingsteignton.* On ye north side of the parish and of ye high road from Exeter to Newton in some coarse fields called Bellamarsh are pitts where they dig great quantities of ye finest pipe clay. There are three of them now in work not far from one another. The surface of the ground where this clay is found is a black moorish heathy soil for about a foot or two perpendicular, below this, via yellow coarse clay which grows brighter and brighter till it comes to ye depth of about 12ft. and then succeeds a bed of perfect white and clean clay, without ye least mixture of stone or sand. It is of a very soft greasy nature, and it is not only used in ye country to make pipes . . . but there are great quantities of it continually carried to Staffordshire and it is found very useful in making their earthenware. The land where the clay is dug is part of the Manor of Preston. The Tenant generally employs labourers to dig it at ye rate of 1s 4d per Tun. They cutt it into square pieces about 1' long and 9" broad and as many thick and of about 35 pounds weight each. In this manner they load it on horseback and carry it two miles to a place called Hackney in Kingsteignton parish where it is shipped on board vessels for Liverpool from which place it is carried to Staffordshire. The owner of the land sells it at ye waterside for about 7/– per tun.

Elsewhere, Milles remarks that this clay 'is more esteemed than that from Biddyford'. Of these workings at Bellamarsh he goes on to say: 'I think the clay was first discovered by one Counsellor Cliff, who lived at Bellamarsh about sixty years ago, but they were then left off, till one Crawford began to work them.'

The Lords Clifford of Ugbrooke House owned much of the land on the east side of the Bovey basin between the river Teign and Chudleigh Knighton, Preston Manor and Kingsteignton. As agri-

* Jeremiah Milles (1714–84), Dean of Exeter and President of the Society of Antiquaries from 1768 until his death. His manuscripts are now in the Bodleian Library at Oxford.

cultural land it was of little value, but it included the major portion of the eastern clay outcrop from which clay has been extracted profitably from the earliest times to the present day. Leases preserved among the Clifford Estate papers and dating from 1750 to the early years of the nineteenth century are therefore one of the best sources of information as to who the early clay producers were and, as the same names recur in the Port Books as shipping clay out of Teignmouth, we also have a measure of the scale of their activities. But the picture is somewhat confused by the fact that they seem to have produced and sold their clay, sometimes individually and sometimes in partnership with each other. The Clifford Estate, in most cases, retained the mineral rights and tenants appear to have paid to the Lords Clifford a royalty of 1s 3d per ton. Except in one case, the leases set no limit to the amount of clay extracted. The exception sets a limit of 4,200 tons from two fields, to be got at the rate of 600 tons a year with an annual allowance of 20 tons for waste. The bulk of the clay extracted during the earlier period was of the siliceous or stoneware variety, but by the end of the eighteenth century the potters of Staffordshire had mastered the use of the finer, white-firing or 'cracking' clays which commanded a higher price. This is proved by a lease of 1809 which stipulates that the royalties payable should be 3s 6d per ton for 'cracking' clays and 2s 6d per ton on all others.

The digging of stoneware clays in quantity created a demand for covered storage accommodation at Hackney, on a tidal arm of the Teign estuary where, as Dean Milles tells us, the clay was carried for shipment. Of the number of clay cellars there, some were built by the Clifford Estate and leased to tenants, while others were built by tenants and held by them on a leasehold basis.

It is a curious fact of history that while it took a Dorset man, William Crawford, to establish the South Devon ball-clay trade on a sound footing, it should have been the Pike family of Chudleigh in the Bovey basin who made the Dorset clay industry so successful. The name of Joseph Pike is among those leasing a clay cellar, then 'newly erected at Higher Hackney', from the Clifford Estate in 1775, and in 1784 he is recorded as shipping 1,262 tons of clay from Teignmouth. It was this Joseph's son, William Pike who, with his younger brother, acquired Furzebrook House, Dorset in 1760 and began buying and leasing clay lands in the neighbourhood. Later, William is reported as living at Bucknowle House, Wareham, with a housekeeper, a 'writing clerk' and three clay-cutters, Sam Bowden, John Collins and Thomas Madge. Here William Pike founded the firm of Pike Brothers which subsequently amalgamated with another Dorset clay firm founded by Benjamin Fayle to become Pike Brothers, Fayle & Co Ltd, a company which is now a member of the English China Clay Group.

William Pike seems to have been the most successful of the early clay producers and merchants, a success which was due, at least in part, to the fact that his career coincided with the rise to fame of Josiah Wedgwood. In 1791 Pike, Wedgwood and a number of master potters in Staffordshire were signatories to an agreement whereby Pike undertook to supply the potters with 1,200 tons of clay annually for five years for the sum of £120, any extra to be charged at the rate of 1s 6d per ton. Furthermore, Pike acted as agent for this syndicate of Staffordshire potters and in this capacity supplied them with clay from South Devon as well as from Dorset. Evidently he continued to keep a stake in his native county for in 1814 we find him leasing a piece of waste ground from the Clifford Estate on which to build a new clay cellar. Joseph Pike, though he followed his son to Dorset, continued to trade in Devon clay; between July 1788 and the following January he shipped over 1,200 tons from Teignmouth.

With one exception, the names of Joseph Pike's contemporary clay shippers mean little to us today. That exception is Nicholas Watts (1742–1806) whose family have been actively associated with the South Devon ball clay industry from that day to this. In this connection the name of Watts became as well known in Devon as that of the Pikes of Dorset. Nicholas was evidently a man of some substance for he owned 88 acres of land in the Manor of Preston.

By the end of the eighteenth century, the trend of the clay trade was for the individual merchants to cease to trade individually and to form partnerships, some of which eventually became the first ball clay companies. Thus, in 1809, Agnes Watts, who had inherited the clay lands at Preston Manor from her late husband, Nicholas, formed a partnership with Samuel Whiteway and several others which traded under the style of Whiteway, Watts & Co. In 1822, Agnes appointed her son Nicholas II (1778–1849) manager of her share in the partnership. In addition to her land at Preston Manor, the partners acquired the right to win clay from certain lands on the Clifford Estate. In August 1845, by a new lease agreement, the Clifford Estate granted to Whiteway, Watts & Co the right to win clay from all the Clifford lands in the parish of Kingsteignton in return for a royalty of 3s 6d per ton on the best clays and 6d per ton on the poorer stoneware clays which are referred to in the lease as 'seggar clays'. The lease went on to stipulate that the amount of clay extracted annually should be not less than 5,000 or more than 6,000 tons, though an amendment of 1853 permitted an additional 5,000 tons of stoneware clay to be got each year.

By 1853 a second clay company known as Blake, Davy & Co was shipping ball clay out of Teignmouth, clay that had been got from the small area immediately to the south of Newton Abbot which was part of the Courtenay Estate of the Earls of Devon. Frank J. Davey had obtained a lease from the trustees of the late Earl of Devon in June 1848 enabling him to get clay in return for a royalty of 4s 6d per ton. Davey proposed to cut 500 tons in the first year, rising to 1,000 tons and 1,500 tons in the second and third years. Five years later, Edward Blake, described as a Potters' Materials Merchant of Stoke-on-Trent, leased 33 acres of clay land on the Courtenay Estate at Decoy for the unusually long term of 31 years. Blake evidently planned his operations on a large scale for he was to pay £1,000 per year rent in return for which he was authorised to 'cut and carry away' 14,000 tons of clay per annum for the first 14 years and 15,000 tons thereafter, any excess to be charged at the rate of 1s per ton. He was to enjoy free use of the 'Devon Wharves' on the river Teign. Soon after this lease was signed, Edward Blake and Frank Davey evidently decided to join forces and began trading as Blake, Davey & Co. In 1856, however, this name disappears and is succeeded by that of the Devon & Courtenay Clay Co.

Returning now to the fortunes of Whiteway, Watts & Co, the original partnership agreement was dissolved in March 1859 and replaced by a new one which was to run for seven years, trading under the same name. This new agreement contained a clause stating that if at any time the firm required to work the Watts family's lands but failed to reach agreement on the terms of the lease, the partnership might be dissolved. The insertion of such a clause suggests that all was not well with the partnership and so it proved. In May of 1859, the company wrote to the trustees of the Watts Estate requesting a reduction in the clay royalties payable by them. Though this letter received no reply, it was assumed that the request had been granted. Imagine then the consternation of his co-partners to discover that their colleague, W. J. Watts (1814–1904) had, unknown to them, granted a lease of the Watts Estate to a new partnership consisting of his son, W. J. Watts II, Lewis Bearne and C. D. Blake. The last named was the son of Edward Blake, the moving spirit in the Devon & Courtenay Clay Co. He had entered the trade at the age of 19 as sales representative in Stoke-on-Trent for Devon & Courtenay.

The reasons for this seemingly high-handed action by W. J. Watts, senior, are obscure. Somewhat naturally it led to a quarrel between the Watts family and the other members of the Whiteway, Watts partnership which culminated in an action in the Court of Chancery and the dissolution of that partnership. In 1860, when the dust had settled, there were three companies: Whiteway & Co, the Devon & Courtenay Clay Company and Watts, Blake, Bearne & Co, a trio which, for over thirty years, for all practical purposes divided the South Devon Ball Clay trade between them. We will follow first the subsequent fortunes of Watts, Blake, Bearne & Co (WBB for short) because it was this company which, by a policy of vigorous and far-seeing management, was not only the largest producer of ball clay but was able ultimately to absorb its two nineteenth-century rivals, as well as other late-comers.

Of the three original partners, each holding a third share, W. J. Watts II was responsible for clay production. Charles Davey Blake, who had had previous experience in his father's business, was responsible for the sales side, while Lewis Bearne, who had had banking experience, looked after the accounts. Other members of the Watts and Bearne families soon joined the new firm. These included W. J. Watts, senior together with another of his sons, R. Y. Watts, and L. E. and Arthur Bearne, the two sons of Lewis Bearne. But undoubtedly the early growth and success of the young company was due chiefly to the efforts of C. D. Blake to expand the firm's market for ball clay. It was thanks to his initiative that the company soon had agents in Gloucester (for the Severn area), Runcorn, London and Tyneside, while it was not long before WBB were shipping clay to many continental destinations including Spain, Sweden, Maastricht, St Petersburg, Riga and Egersund. A Brussels agent was appointed in 1871.

The firm's earliest shipments of clay were made in 1860 under the style of Watts & Co and it was on 20 March 1861 that the name of Watts, Blake, Bearne appears in the port books of Teignmouth for the first time. So successful were C. D. Blake's efforts on the sales side that there was soon an urgent need for more clay land and in 1862 the firm took up a number of new leases on the Clifford, Watts, Templer and Swete estates. One of the firm's earliest clay workings was in adjoining fields known as Zitherixon and Rackerhayes, and it possessed clay cellars at Jetty Marsh and Teignbridge, besides renting storage space beside the Hackney canal. In 1867 it leased the Stover canal from the Moretonhampstead & South Devon Railway Company and from this date forward WBB became responsible for the canal until 1942. The Hackney and Stover canals will be referred to in more detail later.

In its early days the activities of WBB were not limited to the production and sale of ball clay; in addition the company traded as merchants dealing in ochre, 'shining ore',* coal and china clay. The coal business was handled by an associate company, Watts, Bearne & Co, which supplied Newton Abbot with imported coal by barge from Teignmouth. The venture into the china clay trade is of greater significance historically. At the outset, the firm purchased china clay and china stone from producers in Cornwall and sold it to potters and others. One of WBB's early suppliers of china clay was J. Lovering & Co of St Austell and one of their early customers was H. D. Pochin & Co, both names famous in the history of the china clay trade and both perpetuated to this day in the title of the largest Cornish china clay producer—English Clays Lovering Pochin & Co Ltd. In 1873, however, WBB had trouble with their chief supplier in Cornwall so the partners decided to become china clay producers themselves and established works in West Devon at Headon, Cornwood and, later, at Shaugh. WBB thus became the only ball clay company to acquire an active interest in china clay. The venture proved successful and continues to this day when WBB can claim to be, not only the largest producer of ball clay in the UK, but the second largest producer of china clay. From the earliest times to the present day, the firm has specialised in the supply of china clay to the ceramics industry and its new plant at Cornwood which came into production in 1971 has been designed to this end. Today, a small proportion of china clay from Cornwood comes to WBB's Preston Manor works where it is dried and mixed with ball clay in certain body specifications.

While ball clay remained, as it has always been, the mainstay of the business, the impression made by the WBB partners during the last decades of the nineteenth century is that they were eager,

---

* A micaceous type of iron ore found locally and used in the manufacture of paints.

dynamic men, ever ready to seek out and exploit some new opportunity. Granulite, a mineral used in the making of glass bottles, was
added to the list of commodities in which they traded. They obtained their supplies from Charles Geen of Okehampton, who became mayor of that town and was owner of the Meldon Stone
Quarries there. Geen was a lifelong friend of C. D. Blake and he
later became the firm's consulting engineer. The partners also advanced money to the Marland Clay Company in North Devon and,
in return, marketed a considerable proportion of that company's
output. They even considered a proposal to raise manganese ore
from the nearby Stancombe Estate, but in this case the project was
dropped. A close business relationship was maintained from the
earliest days of the partnership with the famous Yorkshire Pottery
of Clokie & Co of Castleford. This was the pottery which had been
founded in the eighteenth century by David Dunderdale, one of the
early makers of 'Queen's Ware'. C. D. Blake, who became a business man of considerable means and diversity of interests, bought
this Castleford pottery, thus strengthening a connection which
survived until the pottery closed down in recent years.

The company's export trade with the Continent of Europe and
with the United States grew steadily over the years until, in 1913, it
was decided that the time had come to dissolve the old partnership
and transform the concern into a private limited liability company.
Movable assets were valued at £30,000 and freeholds, leaseholds
and other assets at £60,000. To enable the new company to purchase these, 45,000 Preference shares of £1 each and Ordinary
shares of equal number and value were issued.* By taking up 15,000
of each, C. D. Blake became the largest shareholder and was
appointed chairman of the new company. The other original
shareholders were: R. Y. Watts, Arthur Bearne, W. J. V. Watts, Dr
Austen A. Bearne and Mrs Ada Louise Bearne. This newly con-

---

* After World War I, this capital was reduced to 27,000 Preference and
18,000 Ordinary shares of a pound each. Of this number, C. D. Blake held a third
of each.

stituted company officially came into being on 1 January 1914 and at the first meeting of the new Board it was decided to move the Newton Abbot headquarters of the company from 70 Queen Street to Park House in Courtenay Park. Park House remains the company's registered office to this day although in recent years considerable additions to the original nineteenth-century building have had to be made in order to house new laboratories and to accommodate more technical and administrative staff.

In common with the other South Devon clay producers, the business of WBB suffered something of a set-back during the years of World War I. Because clay production did not contribute directly to the war effort, the available labour force shrank as men left to join the armed services, while it became increasingly difficult to maintain exports owing to a growing shortage of shipping and the effects of the U-boat blockade. However, these lean war years were followed by a boom from 1919 to 1921 when the price of the best potter's clay rose to 55s per ton from its 1915 price of 25s. As we shall see presently, this boom encouraged new clay firms to set up in business in the Bovey basin, but it was short-lived. By 1929 the price of the best black potter's clay had fallen to between 34s and 40s a ton and the blue variety to from 30s to 32s. 'Brokes' and Saggar clays could command only 13s 6d per ton. First, the bottom fell out of the market for stoneware clays due, at least in part, to leading jam manufacturers adopting glass instead of stoneware jars. Then the United States market, which had led the boom, began to fall away as, in a harsher economic climate, American potters begun using their own domestic ball clays in place of the whiter firing clays of South Devon. These blows were the prelude to the great trade slump of the early 1930s, which brought with it short-time working, and it was not until 1936 that the fortunes of the clay trade began to revive.

C. D. Blake did not live to pilot the company through these difficult years. Having been appointed president of WBB in 1921 he died four years later at the age of 87. He has been described as the most outstanding man in the South Devon ball clay industry to date. Certainly the early success and expansion of WBB owed more to this astute mind than to anyone else. In his later years he became totally blind, but the force of his personality remained to the end. His old friend Charles Geen and the latter's son Harry Geen were nominated as trustees of his considerable estate amounting to more than half a million pounds. At the same time Harry Geen acquired a holding in the company and joined the Board.

Senior executives of WBB are remarkable for their longevity. Arthur Bearne was C. D. Blake's immediate successor, but when he died in 1930 W. J. V. Watts became chairman and managing director. W. J. V. Watts, it will be remembered, was one of the original shareholders of the company in 1914, just as C. D. Blake was one of the three original partners in 1860. W. J. V. Watts was chairman until 1964 and a director until his death on 8 April 1972 in his ninety-first year. The latter's son, W. J. B. Watts, joined the company as director and secretary in May 1939. In 1925, W. J. V. Watts became sole owner of the Watts Estate by purchase and thereupon granted the company a lease on this property for a period of twenty-five years. The company thus acquired rights, either surface or mineral or both, over a very considerable area of the Bovey basin. Much of the land thus acquired had, in earlier days, been part of the Clifford, Templer, Mortimer, Davey and Hatherley estates. Today WBB owns most of its lands freehold; the old landlords, and the practice of paying royalties to them based on the amount of clay extracted, belong, in the main, to the past. The only exceptions are the Church Commissioners and the Watts estate trustees.

The recovery of the South Devon ball clay trade was nipped in the bud in 1939 by the outbreak of war. The effects of this second war upon the industry were even more drastic than the first. The administration of the port of Teignmouth was placed under Admiralty control which meant that exports of clay through the port ceased for the duration and such remnants of the export trade

that remained had to be despatched by rail to other ports. The
company—and the industry as a whole—lost nearly half its labour
force during the war years and by 1944 WBB's annual clay output
had shrunk to a mere 4,000 tons. In these melancholy circumstances
it was no wonder that the company welcomed the opportunity to
sell to the American armed forces a large tonnage of sand and
gravel overburden from its clay lands.

At the end of the war, the ball clay industry, like Britain herself,
was impoverished and run down. It was surprised, therefore to find
that its plight had suddenly become a matter of national concern.
The facts were that Britain desperately needed two things: export
revenue and new houses for her people. The pottery industry had
an export record second to none; new houses meant more sanitary
earthenware and both depended on ball clay. Hence Government
officials became seriously concerned about the health of an industry
about which few of them had ever heard before. The upshot was
that in 1946 the then President of the Board of Trade, Sir Stafford
Cripps, ordered an inquiry into the ball clay industry. The appointed working party began its investigation in January and reported to Sir Stafford on 9 March following. They had been
informed, they said, that the pottery industry (including sanitary
pottery) would need 95,000 tons of ball clay in 1946. They estimated that even if all exports of clay were to be stopped, there
would still be a short-fall on the home market of some 22,000 tons.
To ensure adequate supplies of clay in the future, a prodigious
effort was required, for the committee considered it a backward
industry, using archaic methods. A great deal of the work of clay
getting was still carried out by manual labour under the most
primitive conditions. There were no canteens or other facilities.
There was a serious shortage of labour and there seemed little hope
of making this good from within the clay producing districts. The
committee therefore recommended that the industry should be
encouraged to mechanise and that efforts should be made to bring
in fresh labour from outside.

That the industry was backward at this time was undoubtedly true. Having weathered two world wars, punctuated by the worst trade slump in history, this is hardly surprising. The seeds of many new methods of clay getting and clay processing which are now common practice—the shredding of clay is but one example—were sown in the period between the wars but, because there was neither the capital nor the incentive to develop them then, they remained but small scale experiments. It was not until the fifties and sixties that they came into their own.

For the fact that the South Devon ball clay industry was completely transformed in the course of two brief decades, the firm of Watts, Blake, Bearne & Co Ltd was chiefly responsible. In the process it has grown from a small private company with assets valued in 1946 at £53,000 into a public company with a Stock Exchange value of £7 million. This remarkable transformation has been the achievement of a small management team headed by C. D. Pike who was first elected a director in 1945 while still awaiting release from the forces. He became successively assistant general manager and sales director, then managing director before succeeding W. J. V. Watts as chairman of the company on the latter's retirement in 1964.

Such a name inevitably recalled the Pikes of Chudleigh who made their name by developing the Dorset clay trade, but in South Devon the name of Pike is a very common one and it has not been possible to trace whether, in fact, C. D. Pike is descended from the enterprising William Pike of Wareham. His father, I. S. Pike, like Charles Geen and his son Harry, was a native of Okehampton, indeed his sister Adelaide married Harry Geen. Pike senior was an engineer by profession and, under the direction of Charles Geen, he was responsible for rebuilding and modernising many of C. D. Blake's industrial enterprises. Such works included the electrification of WBB's clay mines and the reconstruction of potteries owned by Blake at Bovey Tracey, Bristol, Stoke-on-Trent and Castleford. It was when he moved to Clokie & Co of Castleford in 1908 that

I. S. Pike decided he had finished roving so, having rebuilt the pottery, he settled down to run it on behalf of C. D. Blake.

After the death of I. S. Pike in 1934, the pottery was managed by his widow. When on the death of Harry Geen in 1939, the Blake Estate passed into the hands of the Public Trustee, the Castleford Pottery was sold to Mrs Pike and her family. Young Claude Drew Pike, having just qualified as a lawyer, became a director and secretary. W. J. V. Watts of WBB also joined the Board. When C. D. Pike's aunt, Mrs Adelaide Geen, died in 1941, the Geen shareholding in WBB passed to C. D. Pike. With the possibility of being able to acquire as his share of the Blake Estate, the Blake interest in Watts, Blake, Bearne & Co Ltd, W. J. V. Watts invited C. D. Pike to join the Board of WBB, and after the war, to become a full-time executive.

With the prospect of returning to the land of his fathers in South Devon, C. D. Pike accepted. He was released from the Army at the end of 1945 and took up full-time employment with WBB on the 1st January 1946. Soon after, he was able to negotiate the acquisition, from the Public Trustee, of the Blake one-third interest in WBB.

As conditions of travel returned to normal after the war, C. D. Pike began to travel widely abroad. He did so for three reasons: to sell South Devon clay by studying on the spot the requirements of overseas potters; to investigate the clay-getting methods of producers in other countries and, closely connected with the latter, to keep a shrewd eye open for new plant best suited to his needs. The fruits of this international outlook were that the methods of getting and processing clay were rapidly transformed by the introduction of new methods and new plant. As a result there was a phenomenal increase in clay output per man. At the same time the clay worker was provided with proper amenities for the first time when a new canteen and an ablutions block were built at the Preston Manor works. At this period the company also acquired a considerable amount of extra land in the Bovey basin in order to ensure that

Page 53 (above) *A typical shaft mine with 'high back'. Note the 'mouse-trap' on the crane to prevent overwinding;* (below) *cutting clay by hand in a shaft mine*

Page 54   (above) *An early adit mine of the 1920s;* (below) *a modern adit mine, surface view*

increased output would be backed by ample reserves. The building and equipping of new central clay research laboratories at the company headquarters was a costly step which had since been more than justified by results. All these developments were financed in the main by retained profits.

A measure of the success of this ambitious and costly modernisation programme was a spectacular increase in the production of ball clay. From 64,024 tons in 1953, annual output rose to 111,277 tons in 1956, the first time in the history of the company that the hundred thousand ton mark had been passed. Equally gratifying was the fact that the proportion of this total exported rose until it reached 69 per cent by 1962. South Devon ball clay was now being sold through appointed agents in every Western European country as well as in the USA, South America, Australia, Israel, India and Pakistan.

By 1963 annual output had reached 154,510 tons; twelve months later it was 246,611. The reason for this phenomenal jump was that in the interim a complex series of negotiations had taken place whereby the Devon & Courtenay Clay Company became a wholly owned subsidiary of Watts, Blake, Bearne & Co Ltd. Already, in 1957, Devon & Courtenay and Whiteway & Co had amalgamated, so this move meant that the three earliest of the South Devon clay companies were now united under the WBB banner.

At some time in the nineteenth century, the Devon & Courtenay Clay Company had passed out of the hands of its founders and into those of the Bishop family. In 1902 a limited company was formed to acquire Devon & Courtenay from the three brothers Bishop. This move was initiated by a firm of bankers, Fox, Fowler & Co, and the first directors of the new limited company consisted of Gerald Fowler and three representatives of the Fox family. Besides a well-known textile mill at Wellington in Somerset, Fox & Fowler also owned Candy & Co Ltd, a local firm manufacturing bricks, tiles and drain-pipes from the coarser quality of South Devon clay.

D

In 1904, Devon & Courtenay was taken over by Candy & Co, although it still retained its title and in 1916 the Fox family brought the brothers E. A. and H. O. Jones down from Stoke-on-Trent to manage these two companies. Devon & Courtenay's clay-getting activities had so far been confined to the 33 acres of the Courtenay Estate in the vicinity of Decoy to the south of Newton Abbot, but by the 1920s it became clear that, so far as clay of good quality was concerned, this source was within sight of exhaustion* and the company began to seek further clay lands in the Bovey basin proper. In 1929 it acquired land at Little Bradley, near the village of Heathfield at the northern end of the basin, and in 1932 it purchased the West Golds property to the west of the Teign just north of Newton Abbot. Yet evidently the Fox family still felt that the company's reserves were insufficient for in 1945 they purchased Whiteway & Co which, in January 1946, became, like Devon & Courtenay, a wholly-owned subsidiary of Candy & Co. In 1957, however, the two firms were amalgamated and the firm of Whiteway & Co then only retained a nominal identity; as a trading company it ceased to exist.

Whiteways was not a large company, but it had attracted the Fox family because it either owned or leased several promising clay fields in the Bovey basin. It remained to the last a family business. When John Hayman Whiteway, the last of that name to be associated with the business, died in 1881, his widow asked her nephew, Dr W. H. Wilkinson of London, if he could come down to Devon and run the clay company; she also offered to make him her heir on condition that he adopted the name of Whiteway. The doctor complied; he settled in Devon, changing his name by deed poll to Whiteway-Wilkinson. In 1905, he formed Whiteway & Co into a limited liability company with himself as chairman and his three sons on the Board. One of the latter, William Herbert Whiteway-

---

* No clay working has been carried out in this area since 1966, but this is not to say that further clay may not be extracted from it in the future. For this reason WBB is anxious to ensure that the land concerned is not sterilised by new surface development.

Wilkinson, was managing director. The registered office of the company was at Oakford, Kingsteignton and its clay workings were at Daisypark, Homers Lane, Abbrook and Horsemills.

That the greatest annual clay output Whiteways ever achieved was 33,647 tons in 1910 will give an idea of the scale of the company's operations. It was ill-equipped to withstand the disastrous effects of two world wars with a trade slump in between. In the slump, the firm's production sank to only 10,822 tons in 1931; men had to be laid off and production concentrated at Horsemills, the company's other workings being closed. However, during the 1930s Whiteways began to climb out of this trough and were working a new bed of good quality clay at Chudleigh Knighton. But finances still gave cause for concern and during World War II the situation became desperate. By 1944 the output of clay had dropped below 4,000 tons and in the following year it was decided to offer the business for sale.

The 1964 acquisition by Watts, Blake, Bearne & Co Ltd of these two old established clay producing firms from their holding company, Candy & Co, involved some complex negotiations. Candy & Co owned tile works and pipe-making works* and they were anxious to sell the latter along with the clay producing companies. WBB agreed to this and the pipe producing assets, under the name of Devon Clay Products Ltd, were transferred to Whiteway & Co which thus became a pipe-making subsidiary of WBB. WBB next approached Hexter, Humpherson & Co, an old firm of potters' merchants† who also operated a local pipe-producing business, to ask if they would sell their pipe-making activity. The answer was yes, and under the name of Astatic Pipes Ltd, this also was transferred to Whiteway & Co. The name of the latter was thereupon changed to Western Pipes Ltd which meant that, so far as the clay

* Candy & Co also owned a large open clay pit at Heathfield, but no white-firing clays were got from it. It was used for salt glazed ware, bricks, pipes, paving blocks and fire-bricks.

† Hexter, Humpherson & Co also owned land in the Bovey basin presumably a legacy of past clay-getting activities (see p 63) and this was acquired by WBB at the same time.

industry was concerned, the name of Whiteway finally died. WBB closed down the pipe works in 1970, but the Fox family continue to operate the tile works.

The amalgamations of 1964 could not have been accomplished without extra finance and the capital of WBB was increased to £620,000. Such growth also created a demand for more office space, and Camborne House, No 17 Courtenay Park, was purchased in 1965 to house the engineering and drawing office departments. In this year, WBB also formed a new subsidiary, WBB Sales Ltd to handle clay sales in Staffordshire and two representatives of WBB's former agents in the Potteries were appointed directors of this new company.

Having come so far so fast, the directors of WBB might have been forgiven for resting on their oars for a well-earned breather. This is the practice euphemistically referred to in company reports as 'a period of consolidation'. For WBB there was to be no such period. On the contrary, the board decided that to finance future expansion plans it was necessary for the company to become a public one. Accordingly, on 9 December 1966, 628,000 Ordinary shares of 5s each were offered to the public. This issue was over-subscribed some fifteen times. Thus WBB became one of the very few public companies operating wholly in Devonshire.

In 1967, the company acquired the freehold of all its china clay minerals and processing plant at Cornwood and Shaugh in West Devon. Nevertheless, it was decided to concentrate on the ball clay side of the business for the time being owing to the refusal of the government to include the Devon china clay activity in the Development Area which they had created in the Cornish china clay district. This refusal was naturally prejudicial where the Devonshire producers were concerned. Although china clay is not the subject of this book, it may be said that, despite this handicap, WBB's china clay activity has made remarkable progress in the last few years.

Another move made in 1967 was the purchase of a considerable shareholding in the North Devon Clay Company Ltd on the strength of which C. D. Pike became a director of that company. In the following year, by purchase and by exchange of shares, WBB increased its holding to 100 per cent which meant that the Group (as we must now call WBB) now had a wholly-owned subsidiary operating in the North Devon clay field in the parish of Peters Marland. It also made several purchases of land in the Bovey basin at this time. One of these was part of Sandford Orleigh farm on the west bank of the Teign a little to the north of Newton Abbot. It is here that WBB have sunk the latest and most modern of its clay mines. On high ground overlooking the surface buildings of this mine and with a fine view over the whole of the Bovey basin is the Group's new Training Centre at Little Whitehill. This house having been acquired, it was adapted to relieve the pressure on group headquarters at Courtenay Park which, despite further additions, was becoming over congested.

In 1969, Newton Abbot Clays Ltd was acquired by the WBB Group. This company had been born in 1919, a fruit of the optimism engendered by that first all too brief post-war boom period. It had therefore had an independent working life of almost exactly fifty years. A private limited company with an original capital of £10,000, it was founded originally to take over the assets of a small private clay concern known as Browne, Goddard & Co which, under the name of Browne & Sons had begun extracting and shipping clay from land on the Clifford Estate in 1872. The new limited company was first registered on 28 February 1919 with an office at Biddick's Court, St Austell which was later moved to High Cross Street in the same town. Finally, 'Lovering Lodge' at East Gold Marshes became the firm's headquarters.

If the reader suspects from the foregoing that the Cornish china clay industry was involved in the birth of Newton Abbot Clays he will not be wrong. Its two founders, R. R. French and E. J. Hancock, were both well known in the Cornish china clay works and it was not very long before they were joined on the new company's board by John Lovering, while when the company's capital was

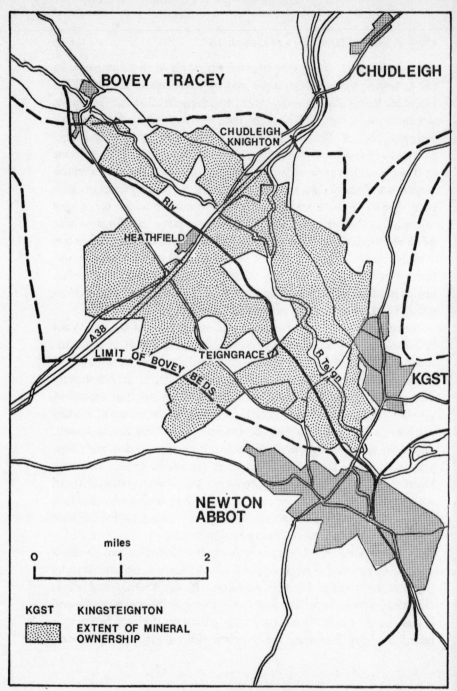

BOVEY TRACEY

CHUDLEIGH

CHUDLEIGH
KNIGHTON

Rly

HEATHFIELD

A38

LIMIT OF BOVEY BEDS

TEIGNGRACE

R Teign

KGST

NEWTON
ABBOT

miles

0   1   2

KGST   KINGSTEIGNTON
        EXTENT OF MINERAL
        OWNERSHIP

Land owned or worked by WBB

increased several other members of the Lovering family became shareholders. French and Hancock had acquired land at Bellamarsh from the Clifford Estate and, being a newcomer, the company made a great effort to build up adequate reserves. In its early days it indulged in a protracted search for good clay-bearing ground which proved only partly successful. Soon the company was working clay at Chudleigh Knighton, at Kingsmeadow, beside the Newton Abbot–Chudleigh road opposite Abbrook, at Homers Lane and at East Gold Marshes. With one exception, however, the clays found were siliceous and following the slump in the demand for stoneware clays the various clay workings were closed one by one, Homers Lane in 1923, Chudleigh Knighton in 1926. The leases of Bellamarsh and Kingsmeadow were given up in 1929 and 1931. The one exception was East Golds where clay of really good quality and quantity was found and consequently it was here that the company concentrated its activities for the remainder of its independent existence, although it began to develop new workings at the adjoining Pinsents Marsh in 1954.

In 1944, by agreement between Newton Abbot Clays and R. C. F. Whiteway-Wilkinson and others, an enterprise known as the Mid-Devon Washed Sand and Ballast Co was formed. The purpose of the company was to act as an outlet for the saleable sand and gravel in the overburden from East Golds and elsewhere. This activity is now the responsibility of Newton Abbot Clays, but operating under the style of the WBB Sand and Gravel Company.

In the effort to compete with its older neighbours, the company was responsible for introducing a number of innovations in the field of clay getting and clay processing. It had good connections with the American Market, and it was in answer to a demand from that quarter that the company produced the first shredded clay in 1938. This activity marked time until after the war when, in 1948, an improved shredding machine was introduced, and increased covered storage space provided, at East Golds. In 1947, the company introduced an attritor pulverising plant. As we shall see in the

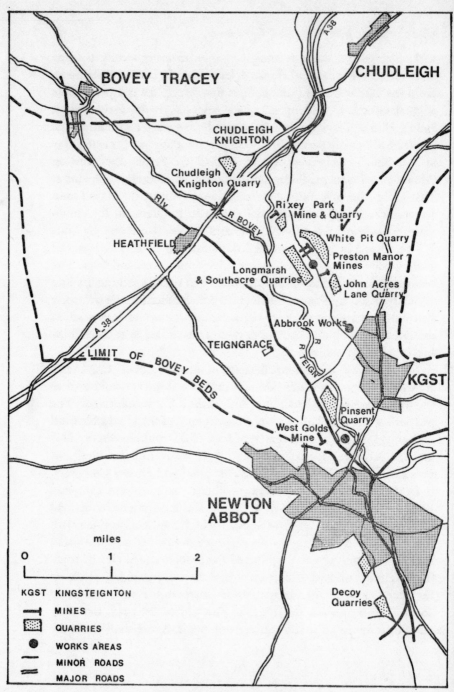

Principal clay works of WBB

next chapter, the company was also a pioneer in the mechanisation of clay-getting. In 1962, Newton Abbot Clays became interested in the possibilities of clay blending, envisaging the future production of complete 'bodies' for potters. To this end, in partnership with North Devon Clays, an experimental 'body pilot plant' was laid down in Stoke-on-Trent.

One last acquisition of WBB remains to be noticed. This is Dorset Clay Products Ltd which became a member of the group in 1971. This is a small company holding only a very small ball clay concession in Dorset. But this latest move has given WBB a foothold in this third ball clay producing area.

The developments of the last twenty years have made WBB the largest ball clay producer in Britain, but anyone who thinks that the group enjoys a comfortable monopoly, even on its home ground in South Devon, is mistaken. WBB's competitor in South Devon is a member of the English China Clays group of companies, until recently known as Hexter & Budge (ECC) Ltd but now as ECC Ball Clays Ltd. It represents the joint assets of three former independent clay producers in the Bovey basin, the oldest of which was perpetuated in the company's title until 1971.

The name of Hexter, Humpherson & Co appeared as pipe-makers on an earlier page and it was from them that the firm of Hexter & Budge appears to have stemmed though the precise connection between them is obscure. In the 1890s, Hexter, Humpherson & Co describe themselves as potters merchants. Between 1891 and 1893 they were certainly exporting clay from Teignmouth and, judging from leases of land granted to them by the Clifford Estate and others, they also produced their own clay. In 1903, Hexter, Humpherson became a limited liability company. That ubiquitous figure C. D. Blake was the chairman of this new company and held a considerable financial interest in it. For some reason—and very confusingly—it was decided to sell the assets of the company's clay business to an unlimited company known as Hexter, Humpherson & Sons. What the precise connection was between this concern and

Hexter & Budge, which seems to have come into being in 1912, cannot be established though the latter seem to have taken over the assets of the former. The Budge of the partnership was Miss Elizabeth Budge, who was C. D. Blake's housekeeper at the time and eventually became his wife. It is on record that in 1912 she purchased some clay land from the Hexter brothers. Hexter & Budge first exported clay from Teignmouth in 1912 but it was not until 1926 that they registered as a limited company, Mrs Elizabeth Blake (*née* Budge) being the largest shareholder. Mr and Mrs Geen became directors on the death of Mrs Blake in 1938. In 1946, the company contracted to supply clay to Hexter, Humpherson's pipe works. It continued its independent existence, getting clay from near Newcross, 1 mile north-west of Kingsteignton church, until 1957 when it was acquired by English China Clays.

Like Newton Abbot Clays, the Mainbow Clay Co Ltd originated in the optimism of the boom in 1919. Its moving spirit was F. W. Marshall who had previously been associated with the short-lived clay firm of Oliver Goddard & Co whose assets were acquired by Newton Abbot Clays. Marshall was chairman of a board of five which included two members of the St Maur family who then owned the Stover Estate. The company held leases to get clay from Mainbow, near Highweek church, and Newbridge. Its independent career was extremely brief, however, for in 1920 the company was acquired by the china clay firm of H. D. Pochin & Co Ltd and by 1923 all the members of the original board had resigned, to be replaced by Pochin nominees. Thereafter, the firm was run in conjunction with another Pochin subsidiary, the Pochin Ball Clay Company.

The last and youngest of these three companies was London based and bore the high-sounding title of the London, Australian & General Exploration Company Ltd. Very little is known about this company, but its object was mining and prospecting for minerals all over the world. It first appeared on the South Devon scene in 1924 when it obtained a thirty-year lease to work minerals at Ringslade, which lies just to the north of the village of Highweek to the west of Newton Abbot. In the following year it acquired a further 9 acres known as Blatchford Fields. It also held mineral rights over part of the Stover Estate. The company's works adjoined those of the Mainbow Clay Company and in 1951 its ball clay assets were acquired by English China Clays and merged with the Pochin Ball Clay Company. In 1960, three years after Hexter & Budge had been taken over, the English China Clay Group transferred all the Pochin Ball Clay Company's assets to this company. Hexter & Budge thus became ECC's sole operating company in South Devon. It had since acquired some freehold minerals on the Stover Estate; also the freehold of the Ringslade Estate, including Ringslade House. Its name was changed to Hexter & Budge (ECC) Ltd in 1967.

Now that the South Devon ball clay industry is entirely in the hands of two large groups there is a tendency to recall with regret the days when there were a number of independent clay producers. Looking back over that period with an unprejudiced eye, however, it must be admitted that the spectacle of free competition was a somewhat unedifying one, especially when the clay trade was bad and competition therefore particularly keen. At such times acrimonious letters containing allegations of price cutting would inevitably start flying between one company and another. The only sphere in which the old companies seem to have acted in concert was that of labour relations.

On the whole, labour relations appear to have been good, for there have only been two strikes in the history of the industry. The first occurred in June 1913 when Jack Jones of the Gas Workers and General Workers Union attempted to secure better wages and conditions for the clay workers. The clay companies, who had always dealt directly with their workers in the past, refused to recognise the union's right to negotiate and all the clay workers in the South Devon field came out on strike. There was evidently some bitterness, for the more militant resorted to sabotage and in an advertisement in the local press, WBB offered £20 reward for any information concerning the throwing down of cranes on their clay works. The clay companies published their current wage scales in the local press, a move which provoked an amusing sequel when a deputation of clay worker's wives arrived at one clay works demanding to know if the published figures were correct. Having been shown the wages book, they marched away breathing fire and slaughter on their menfolk. With the exception of Devon & Courtenay, the companies eventually yielded to the men's demands though maintaining their refusal to recognise their union. So the strike ended on 13 September 1913.

The second strike occurred on 11 January 1932 when, owing to the acute trade depression, the clay firms asked the men to accept a 10 per cent cut in wages. The average wage in the industry at this time was 9s 4d per day or, for clay cutters, 2s 6d per cubic yard. This was accepted by the workers at Newton Abbot Clay Co, Pochin's and the London, Australian, but the employees of the other South Devon firms staged an abortive strike. At Devon & Courtenay, the men accepted the new terms on 27 January and the others followed them back to work three weeks later. In 1936, when trading conditions had improved somewhat, the men's union appealed to the clay companies to restore the 10 per cent wage cut. The seven companies agreed by majority vote to an increase of 5 per cent.

By 1968, the wages structure in the ball clay works, in common with many another industry, had become excessively complex. The minimum hourly rates of pay were agreed by the Joint Industrial Council, but these bore no relation to the actual take-home pay owing to incidence of piece work payments, incentive bonuses and overtime rates. In 1968–9, the employers put forward a scheme which would do away with the cumbersome wage structure altogether and with some modifications, this was accepted by the National Joint Industrial Council for the Ball Clay Industry. Broadly speaking, under this new scheme, all employees are employed on 'Staff' type terms in that there are no longer any payments for piecework or overtime or any bonuses. Instead, everyone is paid at day rate for an average of 40 hours per week and for any additional time worked in excess of 16 per month or 100 per year 'paid time off in lieu' is granted. So far this scheme has worked admirably and there have been no disputes.

Various attempts were made over the years to persuade the clay producers to act in concert over matters of common concern. For example, in 1930, a London financier named F. C. Chadbourne came up with an ambitious scheme to amalgamate all the ball clay producers, but the Dorset companies refused to play and the schemes broke down. Doubtless it was felt that the individual most likely to benefit from the proposal was F. C. Chadbourne. Again, in the depression period an attempt was made in 1933 to form an association of clay producers to regulate prices, but once again the clay companies were unable to agree. It was on the initiative of the government that the trade was finally brought together.

It was soon after the outbreak of World War II that the government made it clear that it would make it very much easier to discuss matters of national importance if there was a single national body representing the ball clay industry as a whole with which it could negotiate. Following this lead, on the initiative of W. J. V. Watts a meeting was called at the head offices of WBB on 21 April 1941 which was attended by representatives of ten clay producing companies from North and South Devon and Dorset. The only firm not represented was the London, Australian & General Company. At this meeting the British Ball Clay Federation Ltd was set up; W. J. V. Watts was elected first chairman, a secretary and assistant secretary were appointed and the annual subscription for member companies was fixed at eight guineas.

During the war years and the difficult post-war period that followed, there can be no doubt that the Federation did some very useful work by promoting better relations between members and between the industry as a whole and outside bodies both at regional and national level. But as merger succeeded merger in the fifties and sixties, the story of the Federation came to resemble only too closely that of the ten little nigger boys. As membership dwindled, successive annual general meetings were asked to approve a proportionate increase in subscriptions to cover administrative expenses. By 1969 the Federation had practically ceased to exist and it now has only two members.

In 1970, C. D. Pike was honoured with a well-earned OBE and in the same year a ceremony took place at WBB's new Training Centre at Little Whitehills which makes a fitting conclusion to this chapter. This was the presentation to the company by the Lord Lieutenant of Devonshire, Lord Roborough, of two Queen's Awards. One of these was for export achievement; the other was for technical innovation in the development of new clay-mining methods. The company's latest clay mine, No 10 at Sandford Orleigh, represents the embodiment of these new techniques. But in order fully to appreciate the great advances which have been made in the last twenty years it is necessary to know something of the history of clay-getting.

CHAPTER THREE

Getting the Clay

BALL clay, like coal or slate, is either got open-cast from large open pits, or by underground workings. This is as far as the parallel can be drawn, however, for so plastic are the upper strata of ball clay that the getting of clay from underground has been aptly likened to mining in a mass of blancmange. This unusually difficult working condition led to the development of special mining techniques unknown in other and better known extractive industries which are all concerned with hard minerals.

It was along the eastern perimeter of the Bovey basin in the neighbourhood of Bellamarsh where the clay outcropped that the deposit was first exploited towards the end of the seventeenth century. During the early years of the succeeding century, production was confined to the line of this outcrop for the very simple reason that hereabouts the clay was most accessible, being found beneath a layer of topsoil whose depth did not exceed 3ft. When this topsoil had been stripped off, the clay beneath was got by methods not dissimilar from those used in cutting peat from a bog, this process of extraction leaving a series of step-sided trenches running along the line of the outcrop. These steps, known to the workmen as 'eaves', were used to assist the throwing up of the clay from the bottom of the trenches. From these trenches the clay workers dug out the clay in a series of lumps or 'balls' of an average size of 9 cubic inches. To do this a series of special hand tools were developed and continued in use until the first half of the present century. These tools were called a clay spade, a lumper, a tubil and a pog. The method of using them was as follows. When the overburden had been removed to expose the clay, its surface was first cut and cross-cut into a series of squares by means of the clay spade which

69

was a weighty affair with a blade 12in long. To facilitate this operation and allow the blade to penetrate to its full depth, water was
slopped on to the surface of the clay from special wooden containers
which were made locally. The lumper then came into use. This was
a heavy form of mattock with its single blade so angled that the
clay-getter could readily undercut and lever up the lumps that had
been partially cut by the clay spade and at the same time leave a
reasonably level surface of clay upon which the operation could be
repeated. Apparently, in the earliest days of the industry the
trenches rarely exceeded 4ft in depth, ie four cuts of the clay spade,
but in any case the clay deposits at the point of outcrop were of no
great vertical depth either. For trimming the sides of the excavation,
for extracting the first lump in a course and, later, for use in underground mining, a lighter version of the lumper was used. This was
the tubil, a name thought to be derived from 'twobill', an old
agricultural tool with an axe blade on one side and a mattock at the
other. Finally there was the pog. This consisted simply of a longish
wooden handle with a single metal spike let into one end and it was
used by the clayworker to spear the cut lumps or balls of clay from
the bottom of the trenches and to fling or heave them to the surface.
When the first shallow trenches began to give place to larger and
deeper open pits it might require more than one worker heaving
with a pog to raise the clay in stages to the surface, making use of
the steps or 'eaves'. A two-pronged variant of the pog, more nearly
resembling an agricultural pitchfork, was preferred by the men
responsible for loading the clay lumps into carts or barges and from
them to ships.

It seems probable that many of these early clay-working tools
were fashioned under the water-powered tilt hammers of the
famous Finch Foundry at Sticklepath, near Okehampton. Like the
scythes and other agricultural tools made at Sticklepath, there had
to be many individual variants of the clay-spade, the lumper and
the tubil to suit the build, strength and reach of the individual
clayworker. For, like all such simple tools, it required considerable

Page 71 (above) *A cutter/loader machine at work in a modern adit mine;* (below) *an automatic mine-tub tipper as developed by WBB*

Page 72 (above)
*Decoy open quarry,
closed in 1965 and
now a lake used for
dinghy sailing;*
(left) *cutting clay in
an open pit with
pneumatic spades*

skill and knack to wield them in such a way that the maximum output was achieved with the minimum of effort. In unskilled or
careless hands, they could become lethal instruments and many
were the injuries so caused in the early days of the clay trade.

On average, 70 clay lumps or 'balls' were assumed to weigh
22½cwt and this figure became the clayworker's ton or 'tally' on
which piecework rates were calculated and mineral royalties paid.
It was also shipped and sold on the same basis, but because, during
the same period, a ton of broken clay or 'brokes' was reckoned to
weigh 20cwt, this, to anyone outside the clay trade, was apt to be
very confusing. Nevertheless, it was not until the 1870s that the
South Devon clay producers agreed to drop the 22½ cwt 'ton' so
far as customers were concerned, largely because shippers refused
to charter on such a basis. The old measure continued to be used
internally, however, until well into the present century. For royalty
purposes, the old 'tally' still survives and will continue to do so
under certain mineral leases until 1976.

During the eighteenth century, the great and growing demand for
their product by the pottery industry forced the South Devon
producers to leave the line of the eastern outcrop and move slowly
westwards towards the centre of the Bovey basin in quest for more
clay of better quality. This trend could be said to have continued to
the present day, and because, as we have already seen, the clay
seams dip steeply towards the centre, this westerly progression
necessitated the development of new techniques. An increasing
depth of sand and gravel overburden, called the 'head', had to be
removed in order to expose the clay seams, while the deeper the
clayworkers delved the more water they encountered. For through
the basin flowed a river that was prone to flooding; not only was the
overlying sand and gravel waterbearing, but the seams of clay and
lignite beneath were frequently interspersed by thin seams of sand
through which water would percolate from the overlying sand and
gravel. These were known to the men as 'lashes' or 'lice', while the
water that flowed from them, frequently smelling strongly of sulphur,

E

was known as 'mundic water', mundic being the local name for iron sulphide (FeS_2).

After the step-sided trench along the outcrop, the next method of extraction employed was the so-called square pit, each side of which measured 24ft. Because of the sand, gravel and plastic clay through which they were sunk, the sides of these pits had to be very

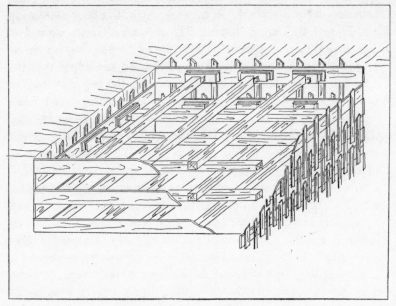

Method of support of square pit

heavily timbered to prevent them caving in. In addition, 'wreaths' (green foliage) or sometimes bundles of heather were rammed behind the timbering. This could not exclude water, but it did prevent running sand from percolating between the timbers. The amount of water encountered in sinking these square pits was quite unpredictable; one pit might remain perfectly dry while in another the volume of water might be such that the pit would have to be abandoned. Such abandonment was not infrequent in the early days of square pits when water had to be pumped out by hand using elm pumps whose barrels were bored out of the solid tree trunk as was the common country practice of the period. As the maximum lift of such a pump was only 15ft, a succession of such pumps might be needed to bring the water to the surface. Apparently between 80 and 90ft was the maximum depth attained by a square pit, and that only very rarely.

Water running down the sides of the pits was collected in gutters known as 'paces'. These were cut with the clay spade to convey the water into a sump from which it was drawn by the elm pump. To ensure stability a width of 12ft of virgin ground on all four sides was left between one square pit and the next. The life of such a pit was necessarily short. When it was worked out, it was filled with the sand and gravel overburden. Then, after an interval to allow the ground to stabilise, the clayworkers returned to the site and worked the 12ft banks between the original pits. This was known as 'working the foursides' and the methods used were precisely the same except, of course, that such pits were smaller, measuring less than 12ft by 24ft.

The tools and methods used for cutting the clay in square pits and foursides were the same as those employed in the earlier stepped trenches. The clay floor of a pit would first be sliced for the full 24ft in one direction, an operation called 'cross-cutting' or 'thirtling', but for some reason the transverse cuts would only be made over a breadth of three or four cross-cuts at a time, a process known as 'long scoring'. When such timbered pits attained any considerable depth it became difficult, if not impossible, to heave the clay lumps to the surface manually with a pog. This led to the introduction of a simple pivoting wooden jib crane called a 'crab' with which the clay was hauled to the surface in a wooden bucket.* The vertical member of such a jib crane was free to rotate through 90° on two

---

* With the exception of the clay-extracting tools already described, all the equipment used in square pits and, later, mines—barrows, buckets and the special water containers already mentioned—were of wood to obviate the risk of contaminating the finer potter's clays with iron, which would impair their whiteness when fired.

metal pintles at top and bottom. The lower and shorter of these fitted into a socket formed in a heavy elm timber laid upon the ground, while over the upper one fitted the metal eyes at the ends of two sheer-legs known as 'tie-backs' which supported the crane. The lower ends of these 'tie-backs' were secured by bolts to timber 'foot-pieces' buried in the ground. Here the provision of alternative bolt holes enabled the angle of the crane to be adjusted if required. It would seem that the first cranes were equipped with a manual winch, but very soon horses were introduced for raising the clay. In order to do so the horse might either pull in a straight line away from the pit, the haulage rope passing round a pulley at the foot of the crane, or a horse 'whim' might be used, the choice depending on the location of the pit in relation to others. Such horses were so well trained that they needed no regular attendant, pulling, stopping and backing at the word of command. When it had been raised, the bucket containing $7\frac{1}{2}$cwt of clay was swung on the crane and lowered to the 'bed-place' beside the pit from which the clay was taken by cart to the clay cellars.

It was the discovery of a seam of particularly fine white-firing potter's clay at Kingsteignton that led to the development of clay mining in that area. Most of the clay got from the square pits and foursides was of the stoneware variety and for some years mines and square pits co-existed. The rectangular vertical shafts of these clay mines measured approximately 13ft by 6ft and, unlike the square pits from which clay of different qualities might be dug as the pit deepened, they were sunk directly to the desired seam. The method of timbering the mine shaft, too, was very different from that used in the older square pits. Instead of massive pine baulks up to 12in square, the lining of a mine shaft was made up of a series of rectangular frames of larch roughly axed to about 8in square. Each of these 'rounds of frames', as they were called, was separated from its neighbour by vertical lengths of timber placed at each corner. The length of these 'studdles' (as they were called) and hence the distance between frames, varied according to the nature of the ground, but generally speaking it was reduced as the shaft deepened. Having reached the desired seam, four 6ft studdles would be inserted to enable the clay to be got and below these would be four more rounds of close set frames to make a sump for water. Planks laid on top of this sump formed the shaft bottom. These rectangular shafts were divided by 'crossboards' into two compartments, one for raising the clay and the other housing the pump and the ladders used for access. As in the square pits, 'wreaths' or bundles of heather to check runs of sand were rammed behind the timbering. Such runs could be sufficiently serious and extensive as to make the surrounding ground so unstable that a mine would have to be abandoned.

At first, the method of clay getting from these mine shafts was similar to that employed in the old bell-pits of the Midland coal-field. In other words as much clay as possible was quarried from the base of the shaft and then the mine was abandoned. Very soon, however, it became the practice to drive short, heavily timbered roadways from either side of the shaft bottom into the clay seam for a distance of about 100ft. The size of these roadways was normally 5½ft high by 4ft wide inside the supports. From a point about mid-way along them, branch headings fanned out into the clay to right and left of the main roadway but mainly on the 'rise' rather than on the 'dip' side of the seam. As the method of conveying the clay lumps from the working face to the shaft bottom was by wheel-barrow it was obviously undesirable for headings to follow the steep dip of the seam. So plastic was the clay that, despite the close timbering of roof, floor and sides of the headings, it would exude through the joints between the timbers and when abandoned and the supports removed, a heading could close up completely in a matter of days without causing any visible fracture of the surrounding clay.

The average life of such a mine, which might be anything from 50ft to 150ft deep, was two years. By that time, provided the run of the clay seam allowed, the area of clay extracted by this 'fan' method of working took roughly the shape of an ellipse with the shaft bottom situated towards the dip side of its centre. Very occasionally, however, the clay seam was of such a thickness that, when the timber had been withdrawn from one fan of headings and settlement was complete, a second fan would be driven outwards at a higher level from the same shaft.

Because of the small scale and restricted size of the workings, the number of men employed on one mine seldom exceeded seven. Two men worked in a heading cutting clay with tubils, another barrowed the clay lumps to the shaft bottom where he tipped it into the bucket, while a 'top-ganger' controlled the hoisting crane and was responsible for the pump. For piecework purposes it was reckoned that there were three barrow-loads to a bucket and three bucketfuls to a tally (22½cwt). Sometimes two headings could be worked simultaneously to make the maximum total of six men underground and one above. There was never a second shaft to these small mines and this meant that the men had no alternative way into, or out of, the workings, nor could there be any through ventilation, either natural or forced. It was for this reason that the length of the workings from the shaft bottom seldom exceeded 100ft.

These mines required a more powerful type of pump capable of drawing from greater depths than the old manual type and this led to the introduction of the so-called 'Cornish' pump, a much larger iron version of the older elm pump. A leather-lined piston worked within a cast-iron barrel of between 7in and 9in diameter. There was a clack valve within the piston and a conical foot-valve at the base of the barrel. Flexible suction and delivery pipes led from the bottom and top of the barrel to the shaft bottom and to a wooden chute or launder on the surface respectively. A wooden 'pump horse' was fixed across one corner of the shaft timbering and from this the pump barrel and its piping was hung.

The introduction of this 'Cornish' type pump in South Devon coincided with the application of mechanical power to both pumping and winding. Because of the short-life of mines or square pits and the instability of the ground in their immediate vicinity, the equipment on the spot had to be of as simple, light and portable a character as possible. The power source was situated on stable ground at a distance, driving pump and hoisting crane by means of ropes. In the case of the pumps, a series of vertical rods in the mine shaft connected the pump piston rod with a wooden or cast-iron beam or 'bob' on the surface, and this in turn was connected by single rope to a bell-crank actuated by the prime-mover. For hoisting, the prime-mover was connected by rope drive to an idler pulley at the base of the crane. To hoist, the top-ganger moved a lever which actuated a crude form of friction clutch to connect this pulley to the winch barrel.

A primitive safety device nick-named a 'mouse-trap' was fitted to some cranes. This consisted of a long lever which, in the event of over-winding, was tripped by the ascending bucket with the result that the clutch was automatically disengaged. On most of the later vertical shaft mines, the clay bucket was then tipped into a rail-mounted tub which was hauled by rope drive up an incline where it was tipped. Such clay tips were called 'high backs'.

The return of the empty bucket down the shaft was assisted by counterweight, but the top-ganger could control its rate of descent by a wooden brake block which came into action when the hoisting clutch was disengaged. The hoisting speed achieved was very slow. At first hemp ropes were used, but these soon gave place to wire. In their passage between the power source and the mine shaft, which might be a distance of anything up to half a mile, these drive ropes were guided by a plethora of pulleys mounted on posts or special stands. As the pulleys often suffered from lack of lubrication, their continual screeching and chirruping could be heard from afar, particularly on still nights.

The source of power most commonly used through the South Devon clay field was the agricultural 'portable' steam engine, the Marshall make being particularly favoured. Each such engine might supply power to several pits by driving a number of bell-cranks and pulleys. WBB was an exception to the rule by harnessing water-power. The overflow from Lord Clifford's Bellamarsh flour mill was used to drive a water turbine at Etson Marshes near Newbridge. This water turbine supplied power to a number of clay workings by a series of ropes between a quarter and half a mile long.* A new overshot water wheel was also installed at Abbrook, operated by water taken from the Abbrook at Sandygate. C. D. Blake's old friend Charles Geen, who became engineering advisor to WBB, was an enthusiast for water-power—he was responsible for the early hydro-power installation at Lynmouth.

This cat's-cradle of moving ropes may have seemed a Heath Robinson arrangement but it worked well for many years, rope breakage being the chief source of failure. Sid Bond, for long black-smith to WBB and a celebrated local cricketer and rugger player, became expert in the rapid splicing of broken ropes. Sid was a great local character; he chewed tobacco constantly, could spit with un-erring accuracy at long range, and his consumption of local cider was prodigious.

Throughout the working week the mine pumps were driven night and day, but at weekends they were stopped when all power supplies ceased. For this reason the sumps at the foot of the mine shafts were always made as large as possible in the hope that they would contain the water that accumulated at weekends. It some-times happened, however, that a mine gang arrived on a Monday morning to find their workings partially flooded and had to wait until the pump had cleared them.

The water problem was particularly acute on the West Gold Marshes property of the Devon & Courtenay Clay Company at Jetty Marsh, Newton Abbot. This is situated at the lower end of the Bovey basin, in the tidal reaches of the river Teign, and the valuable clay seams hereabouts are overlaid by a deep sand bed containing much water. In the early years of this century, C. Brackenbury of

* When originally installed by Geen in 1909, this turbine drove a dynamo, but for some reason this installation was not successful, the dynamo was removed and there was a reversion to rope drives.

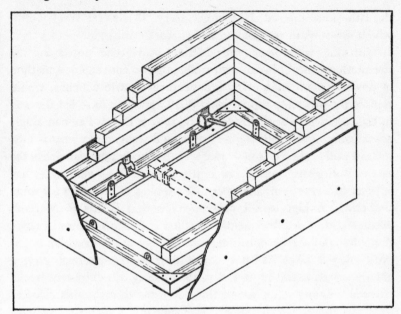

Shaft-sinking shield

Devon & Courtenay overcame the problem of sinking mine shafts through this treacherous quicksand by using a special variant of the 'open frame' method of shaft sinking which has already been described and which was by this time used throughout the South Devon field. Brackenbury excavated and timbered his shafts inside a rectangular protective metal shield. As this shield was jacked downwards through the sand, the 'rounds of frames' were placed two at a time within it. These frames were similar to those used elsewhere, but instead of being separated by vertical corner-pieces or 'studdles' they were set one upon the other with only a thin lath laid between them to act as a water seal or gasket. This method of 'close-framing', as it was called, became the standard practice in the 1920s and 1930s when sinking new mine shafts in that part of the Bovey basin that lies to the south of the Teigngrace road, though the laths were discarded as unnecessary. B shaft at West Golds, which was sunk in 1926, continued to work until 1967.

With the widespread introduction of electric power in the twentieth century it became inevitable that so convenient a method of power transmission using independent electric winches, would replace the unwieldy rope drives. WBB appear to have led the way in this when Pike senior installed in 1905 a Davey Paxman single crank compound steam engine driving a dc dynamo in what is now the saw mill at the Preston Manor works. This engine also drove the saw mill directly. Such a saw mill was—and is—a very necessary adjunct to a clay company to ensure supplies of pit props for mine timbering. A high speed vertical compound Belliss & Morcom steam engine was subsequently installed at Preston Manor in 1936, the older engine then becoming a standby, a situation which lasted until 1947-8 when WBB changed over to the national grid, a change which meant replacing all the existing dc equipment by ac. Curiously enough, the last of the clay firms to make this change-over was the Newton Abbot Clay Company, a comparative late-comer and in some ways the most technically progressive. This company adopted the grid in 1957, though it was not until 1965 that the last of its dc plant was scrapped. The explanation may be that, apart from being close to the power station, as it was a late-comer, its dc equipment was probably more modern than that of the old established companies.

As we saw in the last chapter, the South Devon ball clay industry went through very difficult times during the two World Wars and the period between them. There was little capital available for new equipment and the short boom period following the World War I proved too brief to allow any extensive modernisation to take place. Consequently, despite the coming of electric power and the diesel engine, ancient and modern methods existed side by side and it was not until after World War II that, so far as underground mining methods were concerned, modernisation began. Even so, it was only in 1962 that the last of the primitive Cornish pumps disappeared from a mine shaft at Bradley. The reason for such persistence was that it was by no means easy to find a modern substitute which could cope reliably with water containing so much highly abrasive material. No turbine type of pump proved suitable and compressed air-driven pumps used an extravagant amount of air. It was not until 1956 when a local plant hirer persuaded WBB to try a Swedish type of electrically driven pump known as the 'Flygt' that the problem was solved. These Swedish submersible pumps proved completely reliable and in the mine sumps they could be controlled by automatic float switches, a device which finally disposed of the bogey of flooded mine workings after a weekend break. Modern mine sumps are built in two sections, in one of which the pump is installed while the other serves as a settling tank or sludge trap so that a great deal of abrasive material never reaches the pump at all.

Today, the only examples of the clay-getters' traditional hand tools to be found in South Devon are those which are preserved as museum-pieces in WBB's headquarters at Newton Abbot. And yet, like the old Cornish pump, they survived in use a surprisingly long time. Part of the reason for their longevity was the narrowness of some of the clay seams. This meant that the skilled and experienced clayworker using manual tools could cut selectively in a way not easily emulated by mechanical methods. Nevertheless, a 'tubil' was not the easiest of tools to use in the extremely restricted space of a mine heading, a fact which led WBB, as long ago as 1904, to investigate the possibility of adapting coal-cutting machines to clay-getting. It is scarcely necessary to add that nothing came of this and the universal use of the tubil underground continued in South Devon for another 28 years. It was a famous firm of Cornish mining engineers, Holman Brothers of Camborne, who finally solved this problem when they produced a small and handy pneumatic spade specially designed for cutting plastic ball clay. This new tool was first used in South Devon by the Devon & Courtenay Company in January of 1932 and in the following year the Newton Abbot Clay Company introduced it at East Gold Marshes.

Despite its obvious advantages, however, the introduction of the pneumatic spade was slow. It first appeared when the great depression was at its height and no clay company could afford any considerable outlay on capital equipment. A pneumatic spade may seem a small item, but a large number were needed to equip all the mines in the Bovey basin and all these had to be supplied with compressed air. Nevertheless, their introduction might have been more rapid had not World War II brought the clay industry virtually to a standstill. It was government pressure for increased clay production immediately after the war that led to the wholesale introduction of pneumatic spades. The equipment of a typical clay mine of the late 1950s included a portable diesel-powered compressor at the head of the shaft supplying air to the pneumatic spades below ground. In the headings of such latter-day shaft mines, steel arches, used in conjunction with a timber lining, took the place of the old heavy timbering. Such arches were first introduced by the Devon & Courtenay Clay Company in one of their mines at West Golds in 1951. One advantageous side-effect of mechanisation was that the exhaust air from the new pneumatic spades greatly improved ventilation in the old type of single shaft mines. Where clay seams were narrow and therefore cutting had to be very selective, a bigger version of the pneumatic spade was also used in open clay pits in preference to mechanical excavators.

It was during the 1960s that there occurred a complete revolution in clay-mining technique in South Devon with the adoption by WBB of the inclined adit method which made obsolete the old heavily timbered vertical shafts. A few small and primitive adit mines had been driven in the past, particularly by Devon & Courtenay, as a means of getting clay from beneath the boundaries of open quarries, but these were very small and shallow affairs compared with the modern adit mine. This revolution was in part due to the wide use of new and improved boring machines (the company now possesses five of these) which proved the existence of seams of fine quality clays in locations and at depths hitherto untapped. Another factor was that the Mines & Quarries Act of 1954 made access by ladder illegal in shaft mines exceeding 150ft in vertical depth. It was obvious that the installation of the statutory man-riding equipment in the old type of vertical clay mine would not only be hopelessly uneconomic owing to the small scale and short life of such mines, but also impracticable owing to the unstable character of the ground. Shafts not infrequently became distorted, though not enough to prevent the use of clay buckets or access by ladder. It became evident, therefore, that as a means of tapping clay at greater depths the vertical shaft was ruled out; the only alternative was the inclined adit. The fact that the existing law permitted a limited number of men to work underground in an adit without the installation of man-riding equipment was another argument in favour of this method.

Adit mining began in 1957–8 with the driving of an experimental adit by WBB's mining engineers from the floor of an open-cast working on a gradient of 1 in 2 until, at a distance of 220ft from the entrance, the desired clay seam was struck. Following the dip of the seam, the gradient then eased, first to 1 in 4 and then to 1 in 8. When the adit had reached a length of 1,000ft, its vertical depth below the surface was 250ft. The thickness of the clay seam to be exploited here was 6ft or slightly less and the levels were driven 6ft high and 8 or 9ft wide. Roof support was by timber bars and props set at 15in intervals. Compared with the older shaft mines, these were generous dimensions, yet the floor was so firm that there was no need to support the props upon foot-blocks or, as in the shaft mine headings, to timber the floor to prevent it heaving upward; always provided that the workings were dry and the roadway life did not exceed six months. For it was found that at depths below 150ft, ground conditions became progressively more stable, the clay, while retaining its excellent qualities, losing its natural plasticity and becoming 'short', or 'auzey', as the old miners would have said. Hence, despite the greater depth, less support was required.

If the older method could be described as mining in a mass of blancmange, then the deeper adit mining could be likened to excavating chocolate. Indeed much of the ball clay extracted from these deeper levels closely resembles a dark brand of chocolate in its colour, in its friability and in its slightly greasy surface texture. Unlike chocolate, however, on exposure to air on the surface the clay soon fades to a pale putty colour, a transformation that makes it easier to believe that a substance so unpromising in appearance will, when fired, produce a pottery body of such surpassing whiteness.

So successful did this first experiment prove that WBB is now getting clay from a maximum depth of 400ft by means of five adit mines which have altogether superseded the older method of shaft mining. Later adit mines, such as the company's 'show-piece' at Sandford Orleigh, were driven from the surface and not from the bottom of an open-cast pit as in the first experiment. Sandford Orleigh demonstrates yet another advantage of the deeper adit over the shallow vertical shaft in the mining of clay: that it is possible to site the mouth of the adit on ground sufficiently stable to permit the erection of fairly substantial surface buildings and machinery. Railborne tubs are used for the transport of clay and these are ropehauled up the adit and on to an overhead steel gantry by electrically driven winding gear. When they have been brought to a stand on the gantry, the loaded tubs can be discharged into any one of a series of storage bins below by means of an hydraulic tippling gear operated remotely from the winding control cabin. It was this device, developed by WBB's own engineers, which was largely responsible for winning the company its Queen's Award for technical innovation.

Compared with the older type of shaft mine, the modern adit clay mine is an altogether more elaborate and costly affair with a much higher output and a longer life. It has a planned life of 25 years during which time it will be expected to produce on average 25,000 tons of clay each year. Nevertheless, in none of these respects can it be compared with a coal mine. As in coal mining, work goes on continuously in three shifts, but even in the largest of the new adit mines only seven men per shift are employed underground and it is not considered economic to extend the headings more than 3,000ft from the foot of the adit. In many ways a modern underground clay working resembles a coal mine in miniature. As in a coal mine, through ventilation is provided by means of an 'upcast' shaft which can also be used as an emergency exit. In the first experimental drift mine an old vertical shaft mine was adapted and extended for this purpose and was found to provide adequate through ventilation without the aid of fans. The newer and deeper type of adit mine such as that at Sandford Orleigh, is equipped with two fans, each with a capacity of 10,000cu ft per minute at 1in of water gauge. Such a ventilation system is absolutely essential in this modern type of mine because, surprising though it may seem to the layman, small quantities of both choke damp and fire damp can be present in a South Devon clay mine and consequently precisely the same precautions have to be observed as in a coal mine. Nor is this phenomenon entirely due, as might be supposed, to the presence of seams of lignite between the clay beds.

Lignite might be described as a substance half-way between wood and coal. It is usually brown in colour and, because it is not completely petrified, it still shows the characteristics of the wood from which it was formed. Though it is inferior to coal as a fuel, having a lower carbon content, it is mined and widely used, particularly in eastern Europe. This being the case it may be wondered why the lignite seams of the Bovey basin have never been successfully exploited. In fact, it is said that local lignite, or 'Bovey Coal' as it was called, was used for lime-burning in the seventeenth century. Exploitation has been mooted on more than one occasion in the more recent past, while during the general strike of 1926 when no coal was available, certain clay companies tried the experiment of firing their boilers on local lignite. The last attempt, inspired by the fuel shortage, was made in the 1940s. But lignite has never been used or mined with success in South Devon, the reason being that the seams are thin and the product of poor quality compared with the lignites of the continent, some of which are black in colour and almost indistinguishable from coal.

So far from being an asset, the presence of lignite has been an unmitigated nuisance to the South Devon clay producer both on the surface and underground. On the surface, 'gob' fires would break out on waste tips just as they do in coal mining areas. In 1955 the smoke from a persistent gob fire on a tip at East Gold Marshes brought complaints from local residents, but this trouble has since been cured by ensuring that the lignite is buried beneath a thick layer of overburden.

There is one recorded case where a fire damp ignition in one of the old shaft mines caused a fire so extensive that it could only be put out by stopping the pump and allowing the workings to become completely flooded. But this was exceptional. As a general rule the quantity of gas encountered in the small and shallow shaft mines was negligible and, apart from ensuring that the air was clear after a mine had laid idle for a weekend or longer, the miners took no precautions whatever, using naked lights freely and wearing no helmets. A clay miner named Roberts lost his life in a mine in 1928, and there have been cases where underground clay workers have been slightly burned by fire damp ignitions, but considering the almost total lack of safety precautions, such accidents in the shaft mines were extremely rare. Nevertheless it was obvious that such a happy-go-lucky state of affairs could not be allowed in the deeper adit mines, but the South Devon miners objected strongly at first to the ritual searching for matches or lighters before going underground, and at being compelled to wear helmets with electric head lamps. The fact that Devon clay miners had long been accustomed to consume their candle allowance by having a 'fry-up' in the mine was a strong, though undisclosed, reason for resentment. This intransigence was cured by sending them on a visit to the Staffordshire collieries where they were able to see for themselves that such

Page 89   (above) *German Sürken rotary bucket excavator;* (below) *French Poclain
hydraulic excavator*

Page 90　(above) *Teignmouth c1828, looking up the Teign estuary from George Templer's New Quay;* (below) *transhipping clay from barges to ships at anchor at moorings in Teignmouth harbour*

regulations had long been accepted as a matter of course by their coal-mining colleagues.

Even in the deeper adit mines, dangerous concentrations of choke damp or fire damp are very rare; the latter, for example, is seldom or never present in sufficient quantity to show above the flame in a traditional miner's lamp. Emissions of gas in volume are most likely to occur when a void remaining from some old shaft working is suddenly broken into. For even a very small emission may build up in such a void over the years to create a concentration which could be a source of danger. It is now believed that fire damp may not only be given off by the lignite seams but also, in minute quantities, by the darker varieties of clay which, as their colour indicates, contain a proportion of carbonaceous matter.

The need for selectivity in clay mining makes mechanisation difficult. Nevertheless, after a world wide search for a machine which might be suitable for underground clay cutting. WBB engineers, in conjunction with the German mining engineering company, Westphalia, designed the boom cutter loader. This was initially rail-mounted and tried underground in 1965–6, but then converted to a more convenient caterpillar track system as is in use today. The machine has since been modified for use in various mining and civil engineering contracts. Three are at present employed in clay seams varying between 4ft 6in and 7ft in thickness, and are extremely successful in selecting the clay from between the bands of lignite or other contaminant.

The further mechanisation of clay mining, such as the introduction of the modern hydraulic roof support systems which have revolutionised the coal industry, has been considered, but it was judged that the comparatively small scale of operations could not justify such a large capital outlay. So the use of the timber prop, though archaic in the coalfields, is still the rule in South Devon. This may not be the case in the future, however. With the aid of modern trial boring machines, the existence of clay has been proved at a depth of no less than 850ft. In other words there are immense

F

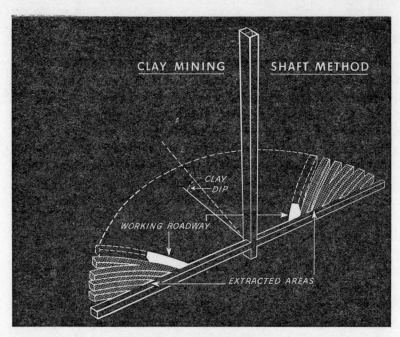

Method of working shaft mine

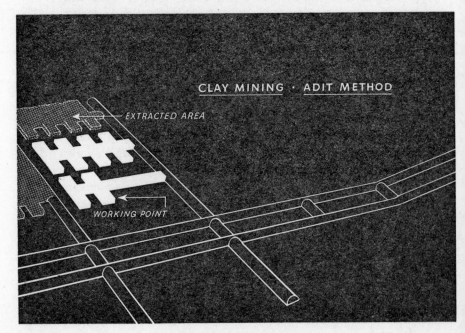

Method of working adit mine

reserves still untapped. Compared with clay cut from open quarries, mined clay is very costly and the cost increases with depth. Today the clay got open-cast from large open pits accounts for the major part of the total output of the Bovey basin, and in view of cost considerations, this situation is likely to continue, relatively small quantities of high quality mined clays being used in blending to improve the characteristics of the clays that can be got more economically.

The getting of clay open-cast on a large scale necessarily dates from the introduction of mechanical excavating equipment. The Newton Abbot Clay Company appears to have pioneered in this field, purchasing a Ruston steam excavator and setting it to work at East Gold Marshes in 1924. In the following year this company acquired a second Ruston machine equipped with a drag-line attachment. No further machines are recorded until 1933 when the Devon & Courtenay Clay Company invested in a Ricter & Pickis bucket excavator. The great value of these machines was the rapidity with which they could strip off the overburden. Apparently the Ricter & Pickis machine was also used for clay cutting but, because mechanical excavators of this kind are unselective, they were of little use for this purpose except in the rare case where a clay seam of unusual thickness and uniformity was encountered. For this reason the extraction of clay by hand using pneumatic spades persisted in open-cast pits until the recent introduction of more precise excavating machinery.

Today, a wide variety of mechanical excavators is employed in open-cast claypits depending on the thickness and quality of the seams. In addition to the older and more familiar types such as face shovels, back-acters and drag-lines there is a diesel-electric excavator specially designed for clay extraction by Hermann Sürken of Germany, and, more recently, the French Poclain hydraulic excavator. The first German machine was a rotary bucket wheel excavator introduced by WBB in 1961 and it has now given over ten years of good service. The French Poclain was introduced in

1966–7 and has proved particularly valuable in excavating the thinner seams because its digging shovel is designed to advance horizontally by the action of hydraulic rams instead of moving in an arc as does that of the conventional type of excavator. WBB's engineers make no apology for their cosmopolitan collection of plant because, in their quest for greater efficiency and higher production, they completely failed to interest British engineers in catering for the special needs of the ball clay industry. It was considered too small beer, so the field was left open to the engineers of Germany and France.

No matter which type of machine is digging the clay, a man can be seen standing above the face upon which it is working, apparently doing no more than idly looking on. In fact, his job is a highly skilled and important one. He is known as a 'selector'. He has an intimate knowledge of the quality and the character of the clay seams in a particular pit, and from his point of vantage he has a much clearer view of what the machine is doing than the machine operator himself, so that the latter works to his signals. Thus although the selectivity of modern clay extraction machinery has greatly improved in recent years, the quality and consistency of the product of open-cast working still depends to a great extent on individual human judgement. For it must not be supposed that the seams exposed in such a working present an appearance as uniform as a layer cake. Far from it. Apart from sudden faults and intrusions of sand, seams may suddenly begin to undulate like petrified waves of the sea, a phenomenon attributed to the effects of permafrost in distant ice ages.

Many of the older pits in the Bovey basin have now been worked out, but despite the use of mechanical equipment, unlike the old shaft mines, the life of some of these open-cast workings can be surprisingly long. For example, of the seven pits currently worked by WBB, that at Chudleigh Knighton was begun in the mid 1930s. The other six are known as South Acre, White Pit, John Acres Lane, Rixey Park, Long Marsh and Pinsents Quarry. Incidentally, it was from the bottom of the Long Marsh pit that the first experimental adit mine No 1 was driven in 1957–8.

As in the underground mines, so in the open-cast pits, the probpen of incoming water had to be dealt with. Here again it is led into a sump from which it can be pumped to the surface and thence conducted away from the pit. For this purpose the Sykes Univac pump was adopted in place of the Cornish pump in 1954 and found to be ideal, though recently, as pits have grown deeper, it has been superseded by the Velovac of the same make and type which has a greater lift. In addition to water finding its way into the pits through faults and sand 'runs', there was always the danger that a sudden flood on the Teign might overtop the sides of a pit with results which could be disastrous. For this reason it was usual to embank the sides of a pit as a protection against flooding, using overburden or waste material for this purpose. Even so, on the belt-and-braces principle, it became customary in some of the low-lying and more vulnerable clay pits to keep a large boat at the bottom which was the clayworker's equivalent of Noah's ark.

The old method of transporting overburden, waste or clay from an open-cast working consisted of wooden or steel-bodied trams running on portable narrow-gauge jubilee tracks. These were propelled either by hand or by horses on the level, or rope-hauled up inclines by means of clutch operated winches similar to those used for hoisting in mine shafts. In 1925 the Newton Abbot Clay Company introduced a method of dumping overburden and waste by means of a rope-worked incline extending from the bottom of the pit at East Golds to a tipping point situated some distance from its edge. In this way a steadily growing mountain of waste was created similar to those seen in colliery districts. Fortunately for the local landscape, however, this 'sky tip' as it was called, remained unique. That it was never adopted by other clay producers was probably due to the introduction of bulldozers, scrapers and similar modern earth-moving equipment. Such machinery has facilitated the strategic placing of spoil in such a way that it could readily be pushed back into the pit by the same agency when the clay had been worked out.

In the same year that the 'sky-tip' was started at East Golds, the Newton Abbot Clay Company installed there an aerial ropeway to convey clay from the bottom of the pit to a bed-place beside the Newton Abbot–Kingsteignton road. In 1937, however, the same company introduced at East Golds the first Muir Hill rubber-tyred dumper trucks. These first examples of a vehicle that was destined to solve the problem of transporting clay between open-cast pit and bed-place or storage shed were adapted Fordson tractors with twin driving wheels and fitted with 2–3cu yd capacity tipping bodies.

To enable dumper trucks and other self-moving machines to operate freely in open-cast workings, roadways have to be con- structed down the side of the pit and on the pit bottom. Where the latter is wet, it may be necessary to lay down a 'corduroy' of timber to prevent machines getting bogged down. Whether it was because the first dumper trucks were under-powered or because the East Golds pit was unusually wet is not clear, but after a few years' experience the firm decided to keep its dumpers on the surface and to install a new and improved design of aerial ropeway. This was supplied by Marcus Hodges of Exeter and was nicknamed 'blondin' by the clayworkers. The wire on which the skip travelled was suspended between two masts, one on either side of the pit. A diesel-driven split winch with clutch control imparted both vertical and horizontal motions to the skip. The contents of the skip were tipped into dumper trucks at the surface for conveyance to clay storage shed or waste tip as the case might be. But although this system avoided the need for pit roadways, it possessed one serious disadvantage. This was that the skip's horizontal motion was strictly confined to a straight line between the two masts and it was probably this inflexibility which accounts for the fact that 'blondin' had no successors. The future belonged to successive generations of improved dumper trucks or tipping lorries operating freely between the pit bottom and the surface. Even so, the old and the new methods, rail-mounted trams and dumper trucks, existed side by side at Rixey Park pit until 1965.

The sands and gravels of the Bovey basin are, over most of the area, covered only by a meagre layer of peaty topsoil. Such land is of little agricultural value and mainly consists of heath and scrub. The flora of this low-lying heathland includes rare plants of great interest to naturalists, but, this apart, its amenity value is not high nor, compared with the beauties of the neighbouring countryside, is the landscape of the valley particularly attractive. It was certainly not improved by the evidence of generations of clay-getting in the shape of used and disused clay pits and unsightly mounds of spoil. It is a hopeful sign of the times very pleasant to record, that the successful efforts made by the ball clay companies to modernise their industry and increase its output have been accompanied by an equally determined effort to mitigate the harmful effects of past and present clay working on the natural scene.

It so happens that England's three sources of ball clay, in North and South Devon and in Dorset, are each situated in predominately rural areas amid surroundings of considerable natural beauty. When the 1946 Report of the Committee of Enquiry into the ball clay industry appeared with its insistence that immediate steps should be taken greatly to expand production, it was by no means easy to reconcile such a demand with the conservation of amenities and other local planning considerations. For this reason in 1949 the then Ministry of Housing & Local Government set up a Ball Clay Standing Conference to consider how the national need for more ball clay could best be reconciled with local interests and amenities. The conference, which was widely representative of the variety of interests involved from river control, highways and forestry to agriculture and nature conservancy, made its report in 1953. This document included a number of recommendations as to how the appearance of the clay working areas could be improved and, to a varying extent, these were acted upon by the different clay companies in South Devon. But it was not until the majority of these

companies were brought under the banner of WBB in the 1960s
that there was an opportunity, not only to plan future production
but also to make good the ravages of the past on a really comprehensive scale. Under the enthusiastic leadership of C. D. Pike, the
company seized this opportunity to such good purpose that its
reclamation achievements won the company a Countryside Award
and are an object lesson to extractive industries everywhere as to
what can be done by forethought, careful planning and co-operation
to secure expert guidance from different local and national authorities.

At Horsemills, Little Bradley, Preston Manor Farm and South-
acre the sites of old pits were reclaimed for agriculture by bull-
dozing old waste tips into them, consolidating the surface, covering
it with topsoil and redraining. Other abandoned pits were converted
into lakes and ponds. The large pit once worked by the Devon &
Courtenay Clay Company at Decoy to the south of Newton Abbot
is now the headquarters of an enthusiastic local sailing club. Other,
smaller disused pits such as those at Abbrook and Rackerhayes are
now stocked with fish and have become the preserves of local
angling societies. Acting throughout in consultation with the Devon
Trust for Nature Conservation, who hold four sites on lease, the
company has found that in such long-term and comprehensive
reclamation work it is quicker, cheaper and better to assist nature
to do the work of reclamation rather than to assume the role of a
latter-day Capability Brown by adopting a policy of wholesale tree
planting and re-seeding which could all too easily create a con-
trived landscape alien to its natural surroundings. Tree planting has
certainly been carried out in consultation with the Forestry Commission in certain areas where the land is too poor to be restored to
agriculture, yet the attractive belts of woodland which now fringe
the old flooded clay pits have come into being amazingly quickly
entirely by natural regeneration. Again, on a barren area at Heathfield which is almost entirely lacking in topsoil, Scots Pine is in
process of establishing itself naturally.

Perhaps the most striking illustration of the advantage of encouraging natural regeneration is to be seen at Knighton Heath, just outside the village of Chudleigh Knighton. Here the large and still active clay pit has been screened by raising banks round its perimeter. The first portion of this bank to be raised was covered with topsoil and seeded with grass. As a result, compared with the dun-coloured heathland which surrounds it, this portion of the bank looks as artificial as the earth dam of some new reservoir. Accordingly, the succeeding portions of this bank were covered with topsoil and then left bare in the hope that they would be seeded naturally by plants from the surrounding heath. The result has exceeded all expectations, for in an astonishingly short space of time nature had done her work so effectively that the surface of the bank has become indistinguishable from its surroundings.

In addition to all this, a great deal has been done to minimise the impact on the local landscape of existing clay working and processing plant. Hedges have been allowed to grow up and trees have been planted to screen these activities from public roads. Young poplars have been planted on both sides of the private road which affords access to the company's latest adit mine at Sandford Orleigh so that in a few years time it will be approached through a tree-lined avenue. The surface buildings of the mine itself have been designed and painted in such a way that they 'disappear' in the natural landscape so far as possible.

Because of its very fine particle size, ball clay processing creates a flour-like dust which, carried by the lightest breeze, settles upon trees and hedgerows to make the vicinity of roads near such plants look much as they must have done on summer days in the pioneer years of motoring before the use of tarmacadam quelled the dust demon. The elimination of this clay dust presented the most stubborn problem, but after five years of trial and error WBB engineers have finally evolved a solution which is now being put into practical effect.

So it has come about that the business of clay-getting in South

Devon, though far more efficient and productive than it was of old, is at the same time much less obtrusive than it used to be. Moreover, the scars of the past have either been eliminated or transformed into leisure amenities which make a positive contribution to the local landscape. Nowadays we have become very suspicious of modern technology because we see all around us the damage which its machines have inflicted upon our natural environment. This being so it is worth pointing out that the programme of reclamation which WBB has carried out in the Bovey basin has only been made practicable by the power of the bulldozer and other modern aids. In the days of the old square pits and the first shaft mines, such reclamation work would have been quite inconceivable. The moral is that modern technology has placed upon the shoulders of mankind a great burden of responsibility. For it has given him a giant's strength and whether he uses or misuses this immense power is a matter for his own judgement. In the Bovey basin today we have a significant and heartening example of what has now become a major extractive industry using its power to heal past scars and to ensure that its present and future activities do no violence to the surrounding countryside.

CHAPTER FOUR

Transport by Water

BALL clay is of high bulk and weight in proportion to its value; hence the cost of transporting it represents an unduly large share of its cost to the consumer. It is for this reason that the question of transport has always been a major factor in the economics of the ball clay industry. There have been innovations such as the shredding of clay and, more recently, its drying, pulverisation and supply in bags on disposable pallets; all these developments have helped to reduce the consumer's production costs in one way or another, yet it is doubtful if they would have come about when they did if they had not also made a contribution to the transport problem either by lessening the weight of the clay by reducing its moisture content, or by cutting the costs of handling and stowage.

The manufacturer of a high bulk, low value article (asbestos-cement products are a good example) can overcome this transport problem to a great extent by the strategic siting of a number of plants, both regionally and world-wide, thus shortening his supply lines. This is something that the producer of a substance like ball clay obviously cannot do because the location of his operations was determined for him by geophysical facts established millions of years ago. Where transport of his product is concerned, it is up to him to make the best of what may be a bad job. In this respect, however, the British ball clay industry has been fortunate in that each of the three known clay deposits is reasonably close to sea transport. Cargoes of clay can be shipped from Poole, Bideford and Teignmouth respectively. At the time the clay trade first began to expand in the early eighteenth century, this was a priceless natural asset, for there were then no canals, no railways and few metalled roads. Consequently the South Devon ball clay industry was en-

tirely dependent for its early success on coast-wise trade through
the port of Teignmouth, which traditionally includes the tidal
estuary of the Teign as far inland as Newton Abbot.

In the passage quoted at the beginning of the second chapter of
this book, Dean Milles described how the clay was carried by pack-
horses for 2 miles 'to a place called Hackney in Kingsteignton
parish where it is shipped on board vessels for Liverpool, from
which place it is carried to Staffordshire'. This was the practice in
the mid-eighteenth century but it did not long continue. The 'place
called Hackney' refers to that point on the bank of a tidal backwater
of the Teign estuary which was nearest to the clay workings. Unfortunately, then as now, the navigation of the estuary was so beset
by shifting shoals and sandbanks that for vessels of sea-going
draught it was extremely difficult, if not hazardous, even for the
small coastal craft of the time. Even at this early date, ball clay was
not an attractive freight where shippers were concerned. It was
usually only accepted as a return cargo by vessels which had
brought coal to some port along the South Devon coast from the
Midlands or the North. Even so, masters would often only agree to
load clay if some local product of low bulk and high value such as
rope yarn, woollen cloth, earthenware,* timber, paper or malt,
could be added to the cargo. It is therefore not surprising that few
masters were prepared to face the difficulties of navigating the
Teign estuary for the sake of a cargo of clay. So loading at Teignmouth became the rule and the clay producers and merchants must
needs be reconciled to the longer overland journey by pack animal
from the clay workings to Teignmouth, or sometimes even as far as
Exeter.

Officially, Teignmouth was not a port at all at this time for the
town did not possess a 'legal quay'. The whole of the tidal estuary
of the Teign was regarded as a mere creek under the jurisdiction of
the customs port of Exeter. Originally one customs officer was

* Rope yarn from Teignmouth, cloth from Newton Abbot and earthenware from
Bovey Tracey.

appointed to Teignmouth with Dawlish, but this was grudgingly increased to two in the eighteenth century. Such neglect may have been a godsend to the smuggling fraternity, who were then very active in the neighbourhood,* but it could cause infuriating delays to the law-abiding. A prime source of grievance was that under an ancient statute Teignmouth was bound to pay what were called 'Town Dues' to the Port of Exeter. Moreover, to add insult to injury, Teignmouth merchants had to make the journey to Exeter to pay these dues, knowing that they went straight into the coffers of the parent port and were never expended for the benefit of Teignmouth. It is small wonder that some refused payment and that there were endless wordy disputes; small wonder, too, that the treasury were under constant pressure to make Teignmouth a port in its own right with its own customs authority. For many years such arguments did not prevail, being steadfastly opposed by HM Customs. Because the customs officers appointed to Teignmouth received commission on the Exeter Town Dues, such opposition was only to be expected!

It was not as though Teignmouth was an inconsiderable port at this time. On the contrary, Teignmouth ranked third after Poole and Dartmouth among the West Country ports engaged in the Newfoundland Fishery trade. This trade owed its popularity to the fact that salt and fish taken by British subjects (together with their by-products) were then exempt from the laws restricting exports. The Newfoundland Banks were fished seasonally from the West Country on the depot or 'mother' ship principle. Teignmouth owed her position in the trade to her ship-building industry and to the fact that, when fitting out, vessels could lie afloat in her natural harbour instead of having to take the ground as they did at other local ports such as Topsham or Lympstone. In 1765 no less than

---

* Large quantities of linens, silks, ribbons, tobacco and wine were 'run' in the Teign vicinity in the seventeenth century and to these were added tea, coffee, rum and brandy in the eighteenth century as a result of higher duties. The final heyday of smuggling in the area came during the Napoleonic war; after the war was over it soon died out.

twenty sailing ships were fitted out for the Newfoundland trade by
Teignmouth and neighbouring Shaldon. This activity meant that
many ancillary crafts such as the making of sails and cordage
flourished in the town, and the harbour was kept busy with the
import of materials needed by these crafts and the stores required
to victual the fishing fleet. 1767–77 was the decade of maximum
prosperity for the Newfoundland trade; after this a decline set in
which was later greatly accelerated by the effects of the war period
from 1793 to 1815. The fact that this decline coincided with the
rise of the ball clay trade was fortuitous. The early ball clay traders
were anxious to expand their markets; in Teignmouth they found
mariners and craftsmen ready to serve them as their old trade
diminished.

Until 1853 the export of South Devon ball clay was prohibited,
so for over one hundred years from its commencement the clay
trade through Teignmouth was exclusively domestic and coastal.
As already noted, early shipments were made to the Port of London
in order to supply the potteries established there under Dutch
influence, but as potters in Staffordshire and, later, in other areas
such as Yorkshire, became increasingly alive to the merits of the
white-firing Devon clays, supplies to London dwindled propor-
tionally and a completely different transport pattern began to
emerge. By 1774 the ports of Liverpool, Hull and Bristol, in that
order, had taken precedence over London, and Staffordshire had
become by far the greatest clay consumer, drawing supplies from
all three of these ports. The superiority of water transport for such
a bulk freight as clay was overwhelming so the prime consideration
was to reduce overland haulage to a minimum.* In this respect the
clay producers found themselves in a far better position than their
Staffordshire customers situated in mid-most England. Their
transport policy was to trans-ship the clay into shallow-draught
river barges which then carried it to the nearest navigable point to

---

* It was for this reason that the sites of so many early potteries are to be found
on the banks of navigable rivers or in sea or estuarial ports directly accessible by
coastal shipping.

the Staffordshire Potteries: from Liverpool to Winsford on the Weaver, from Hull to Wilden Ferry on the Trent and from Bristol to Bewdley on the Severn. Navigation in the upper reaches of these rivers—particularly the Trent—was particularly liable to interruption by flood or drought; nevertheless it was preferable to the difficulties and expense of transport by pack animal or crude wagon.

Of these three ports, Liverpool accounted for by far the largest porportion of clay consigned from Teignmouth, a superiority due simply to the fact that Winsford was nearer to the Potteries than Wilden Ferry or Bewdley. It is no wonder that Josiah Wedgwood was the moving spirit in the formation of the Trent & Mersey (or Grand Trunk) Canal Company whose enterprise remedied this state of affairs. For that company's canal extended from the Trent at Derwent Mouth through the pottery towns, to a junction with the Duke of Bridgewater's canal at Preston Brook, whence craft could proceed directly to Runcorn, the river Mersey and the Port of Liverpool. At the same time the completion of the Staffordshire & Worcestershire canal provided a water link between the potteries and the Severn. Nevertheless, despite these new canal connections with Trent and Severn, the Mersey still possessed the distance advantage. As a result, following the completion throughout of the Trent & Mersey canal in 1777, shipments of clay to Liverpool from Teignmouth doubled within a decade and by 1784 accounted for 74 per cent of the total tonnage shipped. In that year 13 per cent went to London and of the remainder quite a high proportion found its way to Staffordshire via Bristol or Hull because some craft found it convenient to back-load with coal for the West Country from Bristol or from Tyne or Tees, discharging at such ports as Starcross. In the decade 1800–10, Teignmouth clay ships back-loaded a total of 6,700 tons of coal, most of which was discharged in the area under the jurisdiction of the port of Exeter.

Despite the fact that 1784 was the most prosperous year of Exeter's cloth trade, more ships sailed from Teignmouth than from the parent port. Yet it is significant that whereas the clay carried

from Teignmouth was worth a mere £3,000, Exeter during the
same period exported by sea cloth to the value of £550,000. At the
receiving end, however, ball clay shared with crated earthenware
the head of the list of toll revenue-earners on the Trent & Mersey
canal. Much of this revenue was won at the expense of the trustees
of the River Weaver Navigation. Their receipts fell by a half
following the completion of the canal and consequently they sought
to establish a transhipment point at Anderton where the new canal
passed close to the Weaver but at a higher level. This was naturally
strongly opposed by the Duke of Bridgewater and his agents
because it by-passed his canal and so robbed him of revenue, but
latterly, following the construction of a boat lift at Anderton, the
bulk of the water-borne ball clay trade to the potteries passed by
the Mersey-Weaver-Anderton route. Many Staffordshire pottery
firms followed Josiah Wedgwood's example by establishing private
wharves beside the Trent & Mersey canal, hence the persistence of
trade over this all-water route between Teignmouth and Stoke-on-
Trent down to quite recent times.

The widespread introduction of white-ware, or 'Queen's Ware'
by Wedgwood and his imitators combined with the opening of
canals in the Midlands to act as a tremendous stimulus to Teignmouth's clay trade. The 3,626 tons passing through the port in 1774
grew to 9,428 tons a decade later and to over 15,000 tons by the end
of the century. To cope with this increasing demand, the clay
producers and merchants began operating their own barges on the
Teign estuary between Hackney and Teignmouth. They had been
operating on a small scale since about 1760, but now the number of
barges engaged steadily increased. Although the distance involved
was not great and barges could move up or down river only with the
tides, their advantage over pack-horses was not only a saving in cost
but an avoidance of congestion at Teignmouth's old quay. Sea-going
vessels intending to load clay could anchor in Teignmouth's natural
harbour and the barges then lay alongside them to transfer their
cargoes. Usually four barges, two on either side, discharged simul-

Page 107   (above) *Clay barges under sail on the Stover canal;* (below) *clay cellars at Teignbridge on the Stover canal*

Page 108   (above) *Devon & Courtenay Clay Co's wharf on the Teign near Newton Abbot;* (below) *the tug* Heron *with tow on the Stover canal*

taneously, the work being done by men known as 'lumpers' who, wielding two-pronged 'pogs', lifted the clay lumps out of the barges and flung them on to the chutes that fed them into the ship's holds. Later, however, the clay lumps were hoisted aboard in large baskets known as 'maunds' by a simple expedient known as 'jumping'. A rope was suspended from a pulley-block attached to the ship's rigging. One end was attached to the basket while the lumper grasped the other, free, end and jumped from the ship's deck into the barge below with the effect that the laden basket was raised by his own weight. In more modern times the introduction of powered ships' winches naturally put an end to this 'jumping'.

Besides the loading point at Hackney mentioned by Dean Milles, where clay storage cellars had existed since 1751, there were two other clay-loading wharves at the head of the Teign tideway and on the artificial Whitelake Channel. The latter was cut for the purpose of draining Jetty Marsh, but it also enabled barges to get nearer the town of Newton Abbot. The Courtenay Estate owned a wharf at the head of the tidal Teign, just below the present railway bridge, and this was leased to Edward Blake in 1853. The other wharf was above the railway bridge on the Whitelake Channel and was of much more recent date, being built by the Devon & Courtenay Clay Company in 1886. Before the construction of the Whitelake Channel, the Teign Navigation ended in a basin on the site of what is now the railway goods yard. Here that bygone associate of WBB, Watts, Bearne & Co, carried on their coal business in Newton Abbot, back-loading WBB's clay barges with imported coal at Teignmouth.

The effect of the Midland canals on the ball clay industry in particular and on trade generally was so spectacular that by the 1790s everyone had become canal-minded. This was true even of Devonshire where no canal had been built since the Exeter in 1550. Although the overland distances involved were so short compared with those which had prevailed at the Staffordshire consumers' end of the haul, it was thought worth while to build a canal through the

G

Bovey basin from a junction with the tidal Whitelake Channel at Jetty Marsh in order to benefit the clay trade. The author of this idea and its undertaker was James Templer II of Stover House.

James Templer I was a local boy who made good. Born into a poor family at Exeter in 1722, he ran away to sea and eventually made a fortune in India where he was responsible for building Madras Docks. He then returned to his native Devon where he purchased the derelict Stover Estate near the hamlet of Teigngrace. Though extensive, the estate consisted mostly of infertile heathland and the original house, Stoford Lodge, was in ruins. Nothing daunted, James I built Stover House* on a commanding site nearby, using local Dartmoor granite from Haytor. He then settled down to the life of a beneficent country gentleman, planting trees, forming Stover Lake and improving the village of Teigngrace, including providing it with a new church and, true to tradition, a vicar in the person of one of his younger sons.

This was the estate that James Templer II inherited on the death of his father in 1782. The Templer ownership of the Stover Estate coincided with the expansion of the clay trade and it was in 1789 that James II decided that it would benefit the industry and profit himself if he were to build a canal through the Bovey basin extending from the tidal Teign to Bovey Tracey with a branch to Chudleigh. Work began at the southern end in January 1790 under the direction of Thomas Gray of Exeter, but after two years, when he had expended over £1,000 of his own money on the project, James II promoted and obtained (11 June 1792) a private Act to enable him to raise £5,000 by mortgage on his estates. For some unknown reason—perhaps James got cold feet—this money was never needed. By the time this enabling Bill passed into law the canal works had reached Ventiford, a little distance beyond Teigngrace and 1 mile 7 furlongs from tidal water. Here a terminal basin was constructed, for the proprietor had decided to proceed no further. Bovey Tracey

---

* Stover House still exists and is now a school for girls.

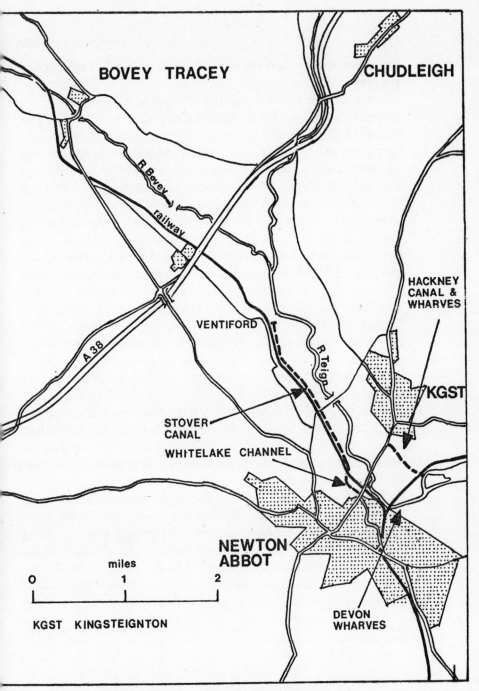

Canals and rivers showing wharves and clay cellars

was never reached and the idea of the branch to Chudleigh was abandoned.

From its junction with the tidal Whitelake Channel, the canal immediately rose 6ft 6in by a double, or staircase lock to bring its bed above the levels of Jetty Marsh. It then continued on the level for 7 furlongs to Teignbridge where the old main road from Newton Abbot to Exeter crossed over the canal, where there were clay wharves and cellars, and where there was a third* lock with a rise of only 6in. These lock chambers at Jetty Marsh and Teignbridge were originally built to a design which was already archaic by the 1790s. Like the old locks on the Wey and Kennet Navigations, they had sloping earth sides instead of vertical side-walls. Locks of this type are cheap to construct but extravagant in their use of water. The reasons for their adoption may have been Templer's desire to economise and the knowledge that ample water was available from the rivers Bovey and Teign and their tributaries. It was just as well that water was plentiful, for despite subsequent improvement works, the Royal Commission on Canals of 1906 estimated that the Stover canal lost 26 million cu ft of water annually through leakage and seepage through its banks and bed.

From the head of Teignbridge it was 3 furlongs to the next lock which was known as Graving Dock. Just below this, the canal's first source of water, the Fishwick Feeder, linked the pound with the Teign. At this point, the lie of the land dictated that the canal should rise 6ft 9in in one lift. Evidently such a rise was judged too great for sloping earth sides, so Graving Dock Lock was built with massive granite side-walls. Whereas the other locks on the canal were all built with chambers at least 110ft long, so that they could accept two barges at a time, this one had a length of only 56ft and consequently it governed the length of barges using the canal. It is tempting to explain this one short chamber as another economy measure, but the top lock on the canal at Teigngrace, 1 furlong

---

* De Salis, in *Bradshaw's Canals*, counts the two chambers at Jetty Marsh as one, which is inconsistent. Elsewhere, he counts each chamber of a staircase as one lock, the method adopted here.

above Graving Dock, is 110ft long, rises 5ft 6in, and also has a chamber of granite masonry.

From the head of Teigngrace lock the canal continued for a further ½ mile to its terminal basin at Ventiford. Here two more feeders entered the canal to maintain the level in its upper reaches. Running out of Stover Lake, the Ventiford brook entered the basin from the west. Straight ahead, and presumably following the intended continuation of the canal, a feeder channel extended northwards to tap the river Bovey at Jewsbridge, near Heathfield, some 2½ miles below Bovey Tracey. New clay cellars were built beside the basin at Ventiford notwithstanding the fact that it was as far away from most of the current clay-working areas as the old tidal loading point at Hackney. Nevertheless, the clay trade of the canal flourished and it undoubtedly gave a boost to exports from Teignmouth although it is doubtful whether much clay traffic ever passed down the whole length of the canal from Ventiford. Writing in 1800, M. Dunsford* stated that the Stover canal carried 7,000 tons of clay annually and that the cost in tolls and boatage from canal wharf to Teignmouth amounted to 1s 6d per ton. Despite the limiting factor of Graving Dock Lock, the effect of the Stover canal was to increase the size of barges engaged in the clay trade. Of the seventeen barges trading on the Teign in 1795, soon after the canal was opened, ten were owned by Charles Templer II including the largest of them with a capacity of 35 tons. Writing in 1904, de Salis gave the average dimensions of a Stover canal barge as follows: length 56ft, beam 13ft 6in, load 30 tons on a draught of 3ft forward and 3ft 9in aft. It seems likely that Charles Templer established a barge building yard on his canal at the outset, that his barges were built there and that this accounts for the name of Graving Dock Lock. Certainly a barge building business at what was locally known as Bully's Basin, between Teigngrace and Teignbridge, survived until well into the present century. This yard was latterly owned by the

* *Miscellaneous observations in the Course of Tours through several parts of the West of England*, quoted by M. C. Ewans (see Bibliography).

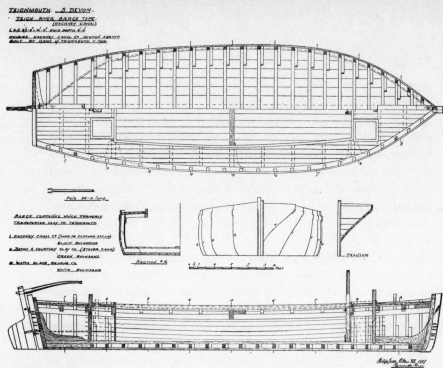

TEIGNMOUTH. S. DEVON.

TEIGN RIVER BARGE TYPE.
(HACKNEY CANAL)
L.O.A 61-5. B. 14-5. HOLD DEPTH 3-6.
OWNERS HACKNEY CANAL Cº NEWTON ABBOTT
BUILT BY GANG of TEIGNMOUTH C 1700.

Pole 26-0 long.

BARGE COMPANIES WHICH FORMERLY
TRANSPORTED CLAY TO TEIGNMOUTH.

1. HACKNEY CANAL Cº (LAND ON CLIFFORD ESTATE)
BLACK BULWARKS
2. DEVON & COURTENAY CLAY CO. (STOVER CANAL)
GREEN BULWARKS
3. WATTS BLAKE, BEARNE Cº
WHITE BULWARKS

SECTION #G

TRANSOM

TEIGNMOUTH. S. DEVON.

TEIGNMOUTH BARGE OR KEEL.
USED FOR TRANSPORTATION OF CLAY ON THE RIVER TEIGN.

SPARS
MAST 29-0. DIA. 5"& 8".
YARD 26-0. · 3"- 2".

APPROX: SAIL AREA 332 ɸ

‡ THIS SAIL IS ONLY USED WITH A FAIR WIND.

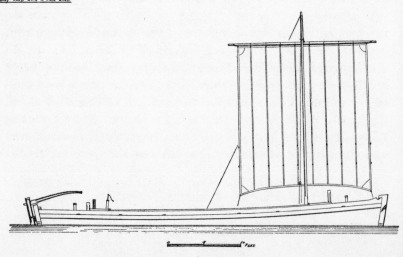

Typical clay barge (*Science Museum*)

Gerry family who continued to build wooden barges to the last, cutting their timber with a pit saw. Until their last days when tugs were in use, all barges carried a single square sail on a mast stepped well for'rard. They shared with the Yorkshire Keel the distinction of being the last craft to carry this ancient Norse rig. When it left the builders, each barge was equipped with a rowing boat for the use of the crew in case they ran aground in the estuary, or for towing purposes.

An unusual feature of the Stover canal is that it never had a horse-towing path. Throughout its long life, prior to the use of tugs, traffic on the canal and on the narrow channels of the upper estuary was bow-hauled by men. On the greater part of the 5 miles of tidal water to Teignmouth, however, bow-hauling was impossible and barges relied upon the ebb and flow of the tides, aided by their sails provided the wind served. If the wind did not oblige, barges had to drift with the tide and consequently had no steerage way. This meant that crews had to correct their course by poling or shafting which could be an extremely arduous occupation. Here, as elsewhere, working this barge traffic became an hereditary trade and the Teign bargemen acquired a reputation for toughness and for their unquenchable thirsts. They mostly lived in the Kingsteignton neighbourhood and were a law unto themselves. The Passage House Inn beside the clay cellars at Hackney was their favourite port of call and, once harboured there, drinking time often took precedence over tide time to the infinite frustration of clay producers and ships' captains alike.

It was James II's heir, George Templer, who provided the Stover canal with a new source of traffic and re-animated the basin at Ventiford. On succeeding to the property he decided to exploit the granite at Haytor on Dartmoor which his grandfather had used in building Stover House and his father in constructing the two upper locks on his canal. To this end he built the celebrated Haytor granite tramroad, so called because its 'plates' consisted of massive lengths of granite, many of which, on the upper part of the line, remain to this day. The purpose of this was to connect the quarries on Haytor with the canal basin at Ventiford. When it was opened, with much jollification, on 16 September 1820, it was 7 miles long, but as the quarries ramified it was later extended to 9 miles, or 10 including sidings. The distance between quarries and canal is much shorter than this, but the difference in level to be overcome is considerable so that the line of the tramway had to take a tortuous course to reduce the gradient.

Having constructed this tramway, in 1825 George Templer formed the Devon Haytor Quarries Company which obtained large contracts for supplying stone to London for such notable buildings as the National Gallery, the British Museum and the old General Post Office. Unlike ball clay, the granite blocks were difficult to transfer from canal barge to sea-going vessels at moorings in Teignmouth harbour and for this reason Templer built (1825–7) what became known as the New Quay there which survived long after it had ceased to fulfil its original purpose.

George Templer appears to have been a generous, warm-hearted and open-handed man. It was these same endearing qualities that made him so popular in the neighbourhood which account for his failure as a business man. Incapable of answering letters or taking important decisions and equally unable to select reliable men for positions of trust in his ventures, he totally lacked the business acumen of his father and grandfather. Consequently, by the time he died in December, 1843, he was impoverished. Although his canal and the granite business appeared to be flourishing and by 1828 the canal was carrying 20,000 tons of traffic per annum, in fact he was already in dire straits as a result of mismanagement; so much so that in January 1829 George Templer sold the canal, the tramway and his Stover Estate to Edward Adolphus Seymour, Duke of Somerset.

The duke was already a large property owner in the district, including land on Haytor which was leased to Templer's quarry company. Following his acquisition of the Stover canal, considerable improvements were carried out, notably the reconstruction, with masonry side-walls, of the old turf-sided lock chambers at Hackney. In this process, the lower chamber of the double lock at Hackney was considerably enlarged and the words 'Duke of Somerset, 1841' inscribed on its west side-wall. In this new form the chamber measured 215ft long by 45ft wide and thus, in effect, became a small wet dock where Teignmouth-bound barges could assemble to await high tide.

Quite apart from any question of mismanagement, the need for the double transhipment of stone—from tram to barge at Ventiford, from barge to ship at Teignmouth—made it impossible for the Devon Haytor Quarries Company to compete with other concerns more fortunately situated. Although it carried on, always teetering on the brink of bankruptcy, for some years after its founder's death, by 1858 the quarries on Dartmoor were deserted and the tramway disused. With this decline and eclipse of granite quarrying, ball clay became the staple freight of the Stover canal and remained so for the rest of the canal's working life. Clay producers had built clay cellars beside the canal at Teignbridge. As most of the clay trade originated from these wharves, the upper portion of the canal, 5 furlongs in length, gradually fell into disuse and decay, the clay cellars built by George Templer at Ventiford becoming ruinous. However, this section of canal continued to act as a feeder channel; in fact, in this capacity it performed an essential service as clay traffic over the lower reaches continued to increase. That Teignmouth clay exports had risen to 19,090 tons in 1838 was very largely due to the influence of the Stover canal.

All this activity on the Stover canal was not lost upon Lord Clifford. That canal favoured the more westerly clay producers in the Bovey basin while lessees on the more easterly Clifford estates were still taking their clay down to the old tidal wharves at Hackney for shipment and were thus at a disadvantage. He decided to remedy this state of affairs in 1841 and proceeded to do so in a very curious manner by permitting—or instructing—his agent, one Henry Knight, to cut a canal through his estate lands, apparently at

Knight's own expense since he was to enjoy the toll revenue. That worthy set to work without, it seems, going through any tedious and costly preliminaries, such as obtaining an Act of Parliament, and the short Hackney canal opened for traffic on 17 March 1843. A tidal lock was built at Hackney capable of accommodating two barges at once, and from this point the canal ran level for 4 furlongs to a terminal basin beside the Newton Abbot to Kingsteignton road. Here new clay storage cellars were built to replace those at the old, tidal, Hackney Wharf which now fell into disuse. Two years later (1845), Henry Knight leased these cellars for sixpence per annum per ton of clay stored to two clay traders, John Hayman Whiteway and William Roger Mortimer. These individuals are said to have been then trading under the style of Whiteway & Co, although it is significant that the date of this lease coincides with that of the new lease agreement between the Clifford Estate and Whiteway, Watts & Co under which the latter were granted the right to win clay from all estate land in the parish of Kingsteignton (see Chapter Two). That the two leases were closely connected cannot be doubted. Under the terms of their lease agreement with Knight, Messrs Whiteway and Mortimer agreed to a toll of 1s 6d per ton on clay carried to Teignmouth via the Hackney canal, while in the agreement with Whiteway, Watts & Co the Clifford Estate stipulated that all clay raised should be shipped via the Hackney canal. The toll seems high for so short a canal and compares unfavourably with the neighbouring Stover canal which charged the same rate for a longer haul. It certainly seems as though, thanks to the co-operation of Lord Clifford, Henry Knight was reclining on a very comfortable monopoly. In the 1904 edition of *Bradshaw's Guide to the Canals*, de Salis names the proprietor of the Hackney canal as Henry Barnes Knight of Hilary House, Axminster, which suggests that the canal continued in the ownership of the Knight family for a great many years, if not throughout its working life.

At some indeterminate date, but about the period of their lease agreement with Henry Knight, Messrs Whiteway and Mortimer also leased the Stover canal from the Duke of Somerset who seems to have become somewhat disenchanted with his new possession as the granite traffic declined. Thus the Stover canal came under the control and active management of ball clay producers, and so it would remain until it was finally abandoned.

As we saw in Chapter Two, it was in 1859–60 that the rift occurred between the partners of Whiteway, Watts & Co which led to the departure of Messrs Whiteway and Mortimer and the formation of Whiteway & Co and Watts, Blake, Bearne. Following this change, John Hayman Whiteway appears to have represented the lessees of the Stover canal. Meanwhile, in 1858, the Moretonhampstead & South Devon Railway was promoted which, from a junction with the South Devon Railway at Newton Abbot, pursued a parallel course beside the Stover canal through the Bovey basin. This meant that the railway company had to purchase land from the Duke of Somerset and, for good measure, the duke sold the company his canal as well. Hardly was this transaction completed when the new owners received two inquiries as to whether they were prepared to sell the canal. One of these came from 'Mr. Whiteway on behalf of Mr. Knight, the lessee of the Kingsteignton canal',* and the other from the new partnership of Watts, Blake, Bearne. From this is would appear that, with the help of J. H. Whiteway, Henry Knight was trying to obtain a monopoly of canal transport in the Bovey basin and that WBB were concerned to prevent him. Nothing came of this move and counter-move, as the directors of the railway company decided it was premature to discuss the question of sale for the present. So the canal continued to be run by its original lesses, whose canal manager was J. H. Whiteway and who now paid their rent to the new railway company instead of to the duke.

In May 1867 the railway company placed an announcement in the *Western Morning News* inviting tenders for a renewed lease of

---

* MSDR directors' minutes, 28 December 1861 as quoted by Ewans, p 41 (see Bibliography).

the canal for a term of six years. To this the existing lessees, Whiteway & Mortimer, replied with an offer of £325 per year which was promptly capped by WBB with a bid of £460. The former probably had no stomach for a fight because they had allowed the canal to fall into disrepair, so much so that they had lately been served with a formal notice from the railway company ordering them to restore it in accordance with the terms of their lease. As it was, in accepting WBB's tender, the railway company ordered their predecessors to put the clay cellars at Ventiford into repair before quitting the canal. This stipulation seems a little hard as these cellars must by then have been disused for many years.

So, in 1867, WBB formed a subsidiary canal company and became responsible for the operation and maintenance of the Stover canal under lease from the MSDR and its successors, the South Devon Railway and the GWR. This arrangement prevailed until 1942 when the company allowed the lease to fall in, the canal then being derelict, no traffic having used it since 1937. From the outset of this new regime there was no canal traffic above Graving Dock Lock and, with the passage of time, clay traffic became increasingly concentrated on the 7 furlongs of canal between the entrance lock at Jetty Marsh and WBB's own wharves and cellars at Teignbridge. In their subsequent dealings with the railway company, WBB acted with great firmness. In 1868 the company inquired upon what terms the railway would agree to a long-term lease. After a great deal of hesitation, the sum of £5,250 for ten years was suggested, a figure which WBB promptly and rightly rejected. The three partners had evidently decided that their original bid of £460 was too high, for in 1869 WBB offered £330 per annum. This was peremptorily refused by the railway whereupon the partners gave notice of their intention to terminate their lease at the end of the first, agreed period of three years. They were evidently confident that there would no longer be any competition for the canal and they were proved right, for the railway eventually caved in and accepted renewal on WBB's terms for the lack of any other bid.

In 1877, when the GWR acquired the South Devon Railway, which by then included the MSDR, they paid £2,800 for the Stover canal and in 1894 there was drawn up the first of three long leases to WBB which between them extended until 1942. This first lease stipulated that the lessees should pay the GWR 1s 8d a ton on Haytor granite shipped from Ventiford. Also—even more optimistically—that the executors of George Templer should have the right to carry in their own boats on the canal ironstone and iron ore on payment of 3d per ton toll to WBB. Mention of such traffics merely echoes Templer's bygone optimism. In fact, although under the terms of the lease WBB undertook to carry on the canal any traffic which offered, apart from an occasional cargo of coal backloaded from Teignmouth, trade on the Stover canal, as on the Hackney, was exclusively confined to ball clay.

The effect of these two canals—more especially the Hackney— was to bring about a great increase in the tonnage of ball clay shipped annually from the Port of Teignmouth. From 19,090 tons in 1838 the total rose to 50,066 in 1868, to 63,860 in 1876, to 86,963 in 1896 and to 102,369 tons in 1905. Of the clay producers, WBB consistently shipped by far the largest proportion of this total; this grew from 16,818 tons in 1863, soon after the firm was founded, to 30,842 tons in 1893. The number of loaded barge journeys per year on the Teign estuary rose from 600 in 1816 to 1,000 by 1854. By the end of the century, this figure had risen to between 2,000–3,000. The effect of the two canals was that the design of Teign barges rapidly became standardised and ownership of the larger fleets was distinguished by the different colours of their bulwarks as follows:

Watts, Blake, Bearne & Co — white bulwarks.
Devon & Courtenay Clay Co — green bulwarks.
Hackney Canal Co — black bulwarks.

WBB had their barges built at Gerry's yard on the Stover canal, whereas Henry Knight, the proprietor of the Hackney canal, had his craft made for him by Gann of Teignmouth. Devon & Courtenay probably had their barges built at Teignmouth. This company's barge fleet rarely used the canals because throughout the period before the 1920s when the area south of Newton Abbot was the chief source of supply, the firm's wharf on the Whitelake Channel remained the most convenient loading point.

The effect of increasing clay traffic, stimulated by the two canals, was that the defects of the Port of Teignmouth, and of the estuary that was technically a part of it, became increasingly obvious. The entrance to the harbour from the sea was extremely difficult, particularly under adverse weather conditions, and was only possible for small craft, while the Teign was badly silted. The Hackney and Whitelake channels at the head of the estuary dried out almost completely at low water and clay-laden barges which failed to leave the two canals on the top of the ebb ran the risk of being stranded for at least five hours. At length the principal landowners and clay producers got together and decided that something must be done to remedy this situation. A certain 'engineer and surveyor' named J. B. West was engaged to make a report on the improvements necessary and an estimate of the cost of carrying them out. The latter came to the modest sum of just under £4,000 and on the strength of this an Act setting up the Teignmouth Harbour Commission was promoted and obtained on 19 May 1836. Landowning interests were represented on this new Commission by the Duke of Somerset, the Earl of Devon, Lord Clifford and George Templer, while Samuel Whiteway II, Nicholas Watts II and Permanos Pearce were representative of the ball clay industry. Pearce, whose family had held clay leases on the Clifford Estate since the eighteenth century, was the Commission's first secretary. When, after three years, the first treasurer died his place was taken by W. J. Watts I, who joined his father on the Commission. Successive generations of the Watts family have been members of the Teignmouth Harbour Commission down to the present day.

The Act authorised the Commissioners to: 'cut, deepen, scour, cleanse, extend, widen and improve' the Teign Navigation from the mouth of the Stover canal down to the sea; also 'to make, build and erect any piers, walls or embankments' which might be necessary to secure and preserve the Navigation 'or the entrance thereof from the sea'. For this purpose they were empowered to raise £12,000 but seem to have failed dismally. The actual total of £2,000 was only achieved by passing the hat round the Commissioners themselves, and even of this meagre sum, the Duke of Somerset contributed half—as well he might as he was not only the owner of the Stover canal but of a sizeable portion of the river bed as well. Nevertheless, despite lack of funds, the channel of the river from Teignmouth to Newton was deepened and improved in accordance with the recommendations of J. B. West, although this navigable channel was not buoyed until 1922. In return for this work, the Commissioners were entitled to a toll of 2d per ton on all freight except stone carried by barge to Teignmouth.

With the improvement of the harbour entrance the Commissioners were much less successful despite seeking the advice of so eminent an engineer as Sir John Rennie. The entrance to Teignmouth harbour consists of a narrow channel bounded upon the west, or Shaldon, side by the red sandstone cliff known as the Ness and on the Teignmouth side by the tip of a long spit called the Den. It is this spit which protects the harbour from the sea and part of the town of Teignmouth became established on its thicker, landward portion which forms a peninsular between the open sea and the natural harbour formed by the Teign. Unfortunately, however, the effect of this configuration upon the river's outflow and the tidal currents was to cause them to create a large and hazardous bar or sand bank just off the harbour mouth which, at low-water springs was covered by only from 2ft to 4ft of water. To make matters worse, the bar was unpredictable; it constantly varied in size and position. It was the existence of this notoriously treacherous bar which, in the early nineteenth century, limited the size of vessels using Teignmouth to 300 tons burthen and made the port unpopular—if not unusable—in winter. The Commissioners planned to remove rocks from the Ness side of the channel and to carry out dredging operations as Rennie had recommended, but nothing was done. It is scarcely fair to blame these first Commissioners for their inactivity, however, when they were not masters in their own house. For Teignmouth was still regarded as a mere creek of the Port of Exeter, and it must have been excessively galling for them to see funds which they might have used to advantage seeping away to Exeter in the form of the bitterly resented Town Dues. As a result, by 1853 the Commissioners found themselves £5,600 in debt, yet in this year Teignmouth was finally freed from its Exeter incubus. In 1852 the Harbour Commissioners had joined forces with the council and traders of Teignmouth in petitioning the treasury to free the port from the authority of Exeter. At the same time a subscription was launched to provide a guarantee fund for passing the necessary Bill through Parliament. These moves at last prevailed against the opposition of the city fathers of Exeter and the local customs officers, and the Teignmouth Harbour Act, which made Teignmouth a legal custom port in its own right, became law in 1853. This event was marked by scenes of great rejoicing in the town. The day was declared a public holiday; a royal salute was fired by cannons mounted on the Den; there was a great procession, headed by a herald on a white horse, bands of music and a long column of marching men including sailors, fishermen and craftsmen representing all the trades of the port. Under this new Act the area of jurisdiction of the port extended from Langstone Point, near Dawlish Warren, in the north to Galmpton Point in the south, a stretch of coast that includes Torquay. Meanwhile the disgruntled Exeter authorities had to be content with a once-for-all payment of £3,000 as compensation. The Act also repealed the 1836 Act by reconstituting the Teignmouth Harbour Commission on a more representative basis which included Teignmouth shipowners and harbour ratepayers as well as landowners and clay companies. Nevertheless, the latter were still well to the fore. John Hayman Whiteway was appointed chairman of the Commission in 1857, an office he held until his death in 1887 when he

Page 125   (above) *Loading clay at Teignmouth today;* (below) *the modern port of Teignmouth*

Page 126   *Rail transport:* (above) *clay loading ramp at Teignbridge on the Moreton-hampstead branch line, 1948;* (below) *modern Clayliner train*

was succeeded in the chair by Lewis Bearne. Meanwhile WBB had another representative on the Commission in the person of W. J. Watts, junior. The third generation of his family to serve on the Commission, he was elected in 1886. The representative of the fourth generation, W. J. V. Watts, was appointed chairman in 1914 and held office until 1965, when he was in turn succeeded by his son W. J. B. Watts, the present chairman. This is surely a remarkable example of family continuity.

Following the passage of the 1853 Act, the fortunes of the port of Exeter declined while those of Teignmouth continued to rise. Difficult though the entry to Teignmouth might be, the entry to the port of Exeter—despite the Exeter canal—was even more difficult, added to which the pilotage dues were higher. Teignmouth's clay trade might be low-rated, but at least it was expanding rapidly whereas Exeter's high-rated wool trade rapidly dwindled away. Another factor which influenced Teignmouth favourably was the coming of the railway.

Authorised in 1844, surveyed and constructed under the superintendence of I. K. Brunel, the Exeter–Plymouth line of the South Devon Railway followed the northern shore of the Teign estuary very closely for most of its course between Teignmouth and Newton Abbot. So much so that the Harbour Commissioners feared that the embankments of the new railway might affect their navigation and once again engaged Sir John Rennie, this time as a watchdog to protect their interests. The railway bridge over the Whitelake Channel was the subject of some discussion between the parties, but apart from this the Commissioners' concern proved groundless and in 1851 the old quay at Teignmouth harbour was provided with a rail connection, ten years before Exeter or Topsham was served by a similar facility.

The effect of rail transport on the ball clay industry and its customers will be dealt with in the next chapter; suffice it to say here that the coming of the SDR appears to have made very little impact either upon the barge trade in clay to Teignmouth or upon

H

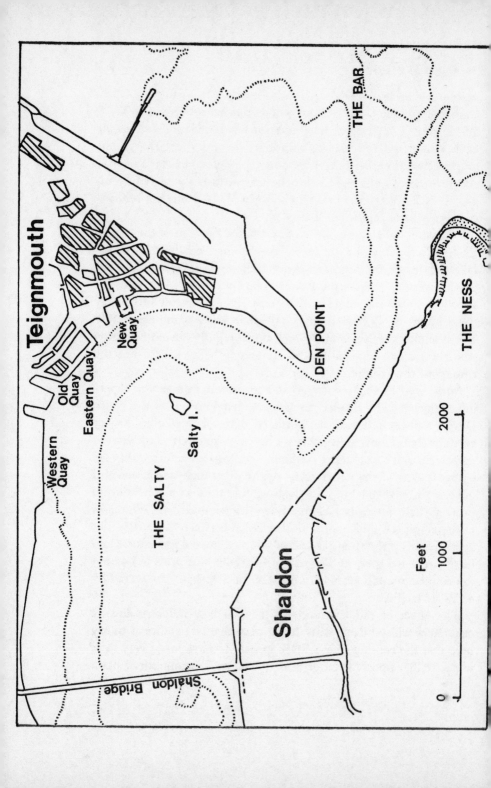

shipments from that port. What it did do, however, was to bring added prosperity to the town and port of Teignmouth, a prosperity from which the ball clay industry undoubtedly benefitted indirectly. Teignmouth's popularity as a holiday resort waxed rapidly with the coming of the railway and the expansion of the town so caused spelt for its harbour an increasing importation of coal and other goods. The rail connection to the harbour initially had a similarly beneficial effect by widening the hinterland served by the port. It should be borne in mind that Britain's railway system was still insufficiently extensive to compete with many traditional coastwise traffics, nor were railway companies particularly anxious to do so, being much more concerned with passenger transport and high-rated traffic such as perishables, cattle and foodstuffs. Thus in its early days the SDR was content to serve the port of Teignmouth rather than compete with it. An excellent example of this was that coal imports at Teignmouth continued to increase year by year until they reached an all-time peak of 43,786 tons in 1876. A considerable proportion of this coal was loaded on to rail at Teignmouth and carried as far afield as Crediton or North Brent.

All this increased activity in the port benefitted the ball clay industry in two ways: by providing additional incentive—and more revenue—for port improvement and by making it easier to charter ships. This last was a limited benefit, however, for the expansion of the clay traffic was such that even when the Teignmouth coal trade was at its peak it was estimated that only one clay vessel out of three was able to back-load with coal. Moreover, the coal trade speedily declined after the peak year of 1876. Railways then began seriously to compete with coastal shipping for coal traffic and also began to carry artificial fertilisers which competed with lime burnt in local kilns using coal. Fortunately, however, by this time the clay producers and the Port of Teignmouth had grown far less dependent on coastal trade.

Since the ban on the export of clay was lifted an export trade had developed, slowly at first but gathering momentum as the nineteenth century progressed until it offset any decline in the coastal trade. The first overseas shipments from Teignmouth appear to have gone to Ireland, Calais and Quebec, but by 1863 Genoa, Seville, Bordeaux, St Malo and Dordrecht had been added to the list of destinations for ball clay. A decade later the European market had widened still further to include Riga, Egersund, Stockholm, Brussels, Antwerp, Lisbon, Leghorn and Rouen. Some of these European markets attained sizeable proportions. In 1883, Dordrecht headed the list by taking 2,330 tons followed by Antwerp with 1,915 tons. A decade later, however, these positions had been reversed, Antwerp taking 6,717 tons and Dordrecht 4,678.

All this overseas clay traffic started its long journey by being loaded into barges at wharves on the Hackney and Stover canals and despite the fact that the Commissioners kept a river gang, under the supervision of a River Surveyor, constantly at work, there were equally constant complaints from the clay companies of siltation of the navigable channel impeding their traffic. This source of trouble eased somewhat after 1883 when the Commissioners invested in a new steam dredger. The state of the river, however, was a minor headache to the Commissioners compared with that caused by the problem of siltation at the harbour mouth. The supersession of sails by steam power* combined with the growth of the clay export trade to create constant pressure for the improvement of the harbour entrance and of port facilities so that larger ships could be handled. The average clay shipment per vessel rose from 92 tons in 1854 to 224 tons in 1900. In 1866, work began on a new groyne from the tip of the Den Point which, it was hoped, by deflecting the currents would check erosion and slow down the rate of siltation. But in this work the Commissioners were fettered by lack of money. They

---

* It is interesting to note that WBB was responsible for the last consignment of ball clay to cross the Atlantic by sailing ship. This left Teignmouth in 1914, a surprisingly late date. It was destined for the Papermakers' Chemical Company of America (later known as Papermakers Incorporated) and a sceptical C. D. Blake doubted—wrongly—whether it would ever arrive.

depended for revenue on dues fixed by statute at 2d per ton (later raised to 2½d) on all shipping entering the port and this proved inadequate to meet the heavy capital cost of the works necessary permanently to improve the harbour entrance. Hence it is scarcely fair to blame the Commissioners for the fact that this problem proved a perennial one.

Just before his appointment in 1892 as Chief Civil Engineer of the GWR, James Charles Inglis was asked to examine Teignmouth harbour and to recommend improvements. Inglis had earlier served as an assistant civil engineer on the SDR before entering practice as a consulting engineer on his own account at No 1 Buckland Street, Plymouth, so he was probably well-known to the Harbour Commissioners. In his Report dated 16 August 1892, Inglis acknowledged that he had been able to draw upon a number of earlier reports. His list included those of Sir John Rennie (1838), Captain Spratt (1856) and I. K. Brunel (1867),* each concerned with the intractable problem of the shifting sandbanks at the harbour mouth. He went on to say that:

> The Denn [sic] Point for almost its entire length has been cleared away down to a few feet above low water, and thus the seas are allowed, from a little above low water on a rising tide, to run right into the harbour.

In these circumstances, the Den could have afforded but little protection to the harbour and this state of affairs probably contributed greatly to the enlargement of the shoal known as the Salty in the middle of the harbour. For, as later investigations would show, the Salty is composed mainly of marine material and not, as might be supposed, of silt brought down by the Teign. To remedy this state of affairs, Inglis recommended that the Den should be provided with a new 'backbone' of mass concrete, 8ft thick, the effect of which, he considered, should be to allow this protective point to reform by the natural deposition of material against this spine. He

---

* The date is taken from Inglis's Report, but he must surely have been mistaken as I. K. Brunel died in 1859, eight years before the alleged date of his report. Either Inglis got the date wrong or he confused the great man with his son, Henry Brunel, who was also a civil engineer.

concluded that the only effective long-term solution to the vexed question of the shifting shoals that blocked the harbour entrance would be to narrow that entrance and to extend it seawards between groynes or training walls. By thus confining the tidal currents and the river's outfall, he argued, their speed would be increased sufficiently to keep the entrance scoured and prevent further deposition. To this end he recommended the construction of a new groyne extending seawards from the tip of Den Point, that is to say it would be built out at a right angle from the new concrete backbone. Inglis suggested that this could be 'stage two' of his scheme and it does not appear that it was ever carried out.

The Commissioners took no immediate action on the Inglis Report. In 1894 they reported complacently that they had 'the best channel they had had for years'. But the rapidly increasing size of ships using their harbour very soon forced the Commissioners to have second thoughts and in 1895 they warned the clay companies that craft exceeding 120ft in length and drawing more than 12ft 6in would not be allowed to moor at the buoys in the harbour. At the same time the Inglis plan for the Den Point was put in hand and completed in the following year.

Evidently this work did not prove as effective a remedy as had been hoped, for between 1901 and 1904 further improvement works were put in hand which included raising the height of the new 'backbone' and, on the opposite side of the entrance channel, blasting away the rocks at the foot of the Ness by means of submarine charges laid by a diver. In 1901, two of the Commissioners, Dr Whiteway-Wilkinson and his son, purchased the steam tug *Bonchurch* to assist vessels entering or leaving the harbour, and they formed a small company known as the Regia Tug Company to operate it. During the subsequent improvement works, the experiment was made of attempting to deepen the channel over the bar by using a form of submerged scarifier towed by the *Bonchurch*. In 1909 the Commissioners purchased a mechanical silt blower in a further attempt to maintain a clear channel.

A typical clay charter for Teignmouth in the days of sail stipulated not more than '150 tons per weather working day' as a rate of loading. This figure was based on the traditional method of mooring in the harbour and loading the clay overside from barges. As the nineteenth century wore on, a change in loading methods became inevitable; larger ships called for a higher rate of loading and were also too big to use the old moorings. As a result, the Teignmouth quays, which in the past had never been popular with a clay industry geared to water transport and reluctant to pay quay dues, became increasingly used for clay loading. The Teignmouth Quays Order of 1887 authorised the construction of 'new quays in the River Teign and other works in connection therewith at West Teignmouth in the County of Devon'. This order led to the formation of the Teignmouth Quay Company which, from that date forward, was to play an important part in the story of the South Devon ball clay industry. A further order made in 1893 defined the extent of the quays, but not their condition which, by all accounts, left much to be desired. The reason was that the Quay Company, like the Harbour Commission, was chronically short of money. It was not until 1932, when the old Quay Company became a subsidiary of the Devon Trading Company Ltd, that the quays were improved radically with concrete wharves replacing the old projecting timber structures. Four berths were eventually provided with mechanical loaders and elevators and ramps to enable tipping lorries to discharge loads of shredded clay direct into the holds of the steamers.

In addition to the harbour tug *Bonchurch*, which was occasionally used on the river, WBB operated the steam tug *Kestrel** and, later, in the early twenties, the locally built *Heron*, which was propelled by a Kelvin paraffin engine, to tow barges between wharves at Jetty Marsh and Teignmouth. The effect of these tugs was to banish the old square-rigged sails from the estuary; at the same time it made

* *Kestrel* was originally registered in the name of Arthur Bearne but it was transfered to WBB when the firm became a limited company in 1914. In M. C. Ewan's book (see Bibliography) it has been confused with the later *Heron*.

clay movement by barge speedier and more predictable, though still dependent on the tides. Despite the use of these tugs and despite the fact that the Harbour Commissioners put down new mooring buoys in the harbour suitable for larger ships, clay traffic on the two canals and the river began steadily to decline during this period between the wars. A number of different factors combined to account for this: the improvement of the Teignmouth quays which placed barge traffic at a disadvantage; increasing competition from road and rail, not only on the short haul between the clay works and the port but for the coastal trade; finally, World War I and the trade slump that soon followed, sadly reduced clay production.

In 1929 the Devon & Courtenay Clay Company made a study of the comparative costs of water and road transport to Teignmouth which showed that at 4s 6d per ton, water transport was 2d per ton cheaper than the road and, on the strength of this, decided not to change. Yet it is symptomatic that, eight years later, in 1937, the company reversed this decision by disposing of its barge fleet on the ground that it cost too much to maintain. The fact that the company lost four barges in the estuary during the exceptionally stormy weather that marked the first four months of 1934 may have had some bearing on this change of policy. The post-war slump in the clay trade naturally spelled loss of revenue both for the Teignmouth Harbour Commissioners and for the Quay Company. The latter was almost bankrupted, while the former sold off their dredger, future dredging of harbour mouth and river being done under contract. In 1930 the tug *Bonchurch* was sold. The Commissioners would no longer subsidise it for harbour use, while WBB, who had used it for towing their barges, now scarcely required it. The Hackney canal fell into disuse in 1928 and in 1933 WBB gave up its cellars and wharves at Jetty Marsh, there being scarcely any traffic on the Stover canal. There are said to have been sixteen barges still at work on the Stover canal, mainly in WBB's service, in 1931, but they were old and gradually fell into disrepair. As no new barges were being built to replace them, the end became inevitable. The company's older tug *Kestrel* was scrapped while her younger sister *Heron* carried on under her Captain Johnston and Engineer Lawrence until 1937 when she fell into disuse because there were no more barges left to tow. In 1940 *Heron* went with other 'little ships' to Dunkirk and was one of those which never returned. In 1950, the Devon & Courtenay Company sold the site of its old clay cellars beside the wharf on the Whitelake Channel to the CEGB. In the following year, the Stover canal made its presence felt for the last time by bursting its banks and flooding the North Quarry of the Newton Abbot Clay Company at East Golds. Because WBB's lease had expired in 1942, the canal had become the responsibility of British Railways. The resulting lawsuit was settled out of court in favour of the clay company which used the money to extend the flood banks. So the river and the two canals which had served the clay trade so well for so many years finally died. Officially, the jurisdiction of the Harbour Commission still extends as far as the lower cill of the entrance lock to the Stover canal. For practical purposes—and not without a profound sense of relief one suspects —the Commissioners were now able to lower their sights. Shaldon Bridge became, in fact, their upper boundary and remains so to this day.

Meanwhile the coastal trade—and the canal trade at the receiving end—had also succumbed to competition from rail and road. A small coastal trade to the Humber ports and to Weston Point at the mouth of the Weaver survived until World War II. As mentioned earlier, the Weston Point trade only survived as long as it did because some of the Staffordshire potteries had private wharves beside the Trent & Mersey canal and for this reason still favoured the all-water route from Weston Point via the river Weaver, the Anderton Lift and the Trent & Mersey. Today, the small quantity of clay that is consigned to Scotland—no more than three or four shipments a year—is now the only surviving vestige of Teignmouth's once extensive coastal ball clay trade.

The growth of the clay export trade through Teignmouth has

more than compensated for the loss of the coastal business. In the first years of this century, before the outbreak of war caused a temporary set-back, exports of clay through Teignmouth were running at a yearly average of 100,000 tons. By the end of the 1960s this figure had risen to between 300,000 and 400,000 tons. As the trend today is towards higher quality rather than quantity, annual tonnage figures may increase more slowly though the tendency to use larger ships will continue. In 1934 the steamer *Jennie* left Teignmouth with 1,100 tons of clay on board, but this was quite exceptional and a record which could only have been achieved on the highest of spring tides. From that date until January 1970 most of the ships using the port ranged from 500 to 800 tons. Ships of this size are now considered uneconomic from a manning point of view so that future clay exports from Teignmouth are likely to be carried in fewer but larger ships, probably in the region of from 1,200 to 1,400 tons.

It was this prospect of greater export tonnages in larger ships that caused a meeting to be organised in 1964 to consider what could be done about improving the harbour. This was attended by representatives of all the interested parties: the Quay Company, the Commissioners, Teignmouth Urban District Council and the British Ball Clay Federation whose spokesman was C. D. Pike. It was decided to consult the Government's Hydraulics Research Station at Wallingford on the problem. The Commissioners had previously consulted Wallingford in the 1950s, but in its report dated August 1958 the station recommended that a model of the harbour should be built at Wallingford at a cost of £10,000, a sum which the Commissioners felt they could not afford. Now, however, the situation was so critical that a second approach was agreed upon.

It was decided that the port should be made capable of accepting ships of 1,000 tons dead weight and drawing 14ft of water on neap tides or vessels of 2,000 tons and 280ft long at high water springs. Because marine insurers will not permit all ships exceeding 1,000 tons capacity to take the ground at low water, as the smaller ships using the quays are accustomed to do, it was also decided to include in the terms of reference the question of deepening the harbour beside the quays and also of increasing the area of deep water to permit larger craft to swing.

Two representatives from Wallingford spent six months at Teignmouth in 1965 carrying out a preliminary series of experiments upon which they reported in February 1966. Very briefly, these experiments consisted of coating coarse sand and gravel with fluorescent paint and then placing it at strategic points on the shoals and shores at the harbour entrance so that the movement of material could be traced. Four tons of material were taken from the beach at the Ness, the smaller particles being coated green and the larger red. Although this experiment yielded much useful information, in order to reach a firm conclusion it was considered essential to build at Wallingford a large and accurate model of the harbour and estuary. Here the effect of variable winds, waves, tides and river currents would all be accurately simulated. The area to be modelled extended along the coast from the Parson and Clerk rocks in the north-east to as far as Mackerel Point in Babbacombe Bay and included the river estuary as far as Newton Abbot. In collecting data for the model, tidal levels were checked simultaneously at six points: at Teignmouth Pier, at Teignmouth western quay, at the gas works above Shaldon Bridge, at Coombe Cellars, which is approximately midway up the estuary, and lastly at Newton Abbot sewage works. Current velocities were also measured at eleven different stations. With this data, construction of the model began in June 1968 and by the following January it was working satisfactorily. Its main section, covering the harbour and 4 miles of coast, measured 125ft by 80ft and there was an extension of this to cover the estuarial portion.

There are three shifting shoals obstructing entry to the harbour and these continue to form despite constant costly dredging operations. They consist of a long shoal known as the Hook, or the Ness Pole, which extends from the shore at Ness Point into the navigable channel. Some distance off the point of this Ness Pole are two further shifting shoals known as the Outer and Inner Pole Sands. When the Ness Pole extends itself so far as to prevent direct entry into the harbour so that traffic is forced to make a dog-leg turn round its tip, river and tidal currents eventually combine to force a passage through it and direct entry is thereby restored. This improved state of affairs is only temporary, however, for in a surprisingly short time the Ness Pole has built itself up again and the cycle is repeated.

In his report of 1856, Captain Spratt had advanced the theory that this phenomenon of the shifting shoals off the harbour mouth was caused by a circular movement of their material which, with but slight variations caused by differing weather conditions, was endlessly repeated. The experiments just described proved that this was an inspired guess. Briefly what happens is this. The Ness Pole is progressively built up by tidal currents setting up along the coast from the direction of Babbacombe Bay as a result of the prevailing south-westerly winds. When the Ness Pole is eventually breached and the direct channel restored, the material cut off from the shore goes to swell the Outer and Inner Pole sands. When the wind swings into the east or north-east, however, a strong tidal current sets in the opposite direction parallel with the line of Teignmouth beach. The effect of this current is not only to add to the Inner and Outer Poles but to drive some of this material across the channel on to the Shaldon shore. Here, the effect of the ebb and the river current combined is to transfer the material down stream to reinforce the Ness Pole, thus completing the cycle that Captain Spratt envisaged.

The provision of deeper water at the harbour quays and a minimum channel width of 350ft promises to be a straightforward enterprise. The Quay Company is responsible for maintaining a deep-water channel 100ft in width from the quays. Moreover, as experiments have shown that the Salty Shoal within the harbour consists of material brought in by the tides and is not caused by river siltation, it is hoped that once the harbour entrance is improved, it will solve this problem also.

The solution to the harbour entrance problem is a much more costly and difficult operation which consists of confining the channel by means of training walls as Inglis recommended. The Wallingford model has effectually determined the optimum position and length for this wall which it is proposed to construct as a rubble mound or breakwater. This whole programme of harbour improvement was estimated in 1971 to cost £300,000. It seems inevitable that, despite the expense, such a programme will soon have to be carried out. Also that the South Devon ball clay industry will have to make a substantial contribution towards its cost because the whole future of the expanding clay export trade depends upon it.

Looking at the busy port of Teignmouth today, one cannot help regretting that most of the little ships which enter the port or leave, deep-laden, on almost every tide, should be wearing the flags of Holland, Germany, the Scandinavian countries or even Liberia. It is a sad reflection that once upon a time all the trade of Teignmouth was conducted in British ships, many of them built at yards in this very harbour.

CHAPTER FIVE

Transport by Land

IN the days before metalled roads when water transport for bulk loads was universal, pack animals, usually working in trains, were almost invariably used to convey ball clay from the pits to Hackney or Teignmouth wharves and from the nearest river port to the pottery to which it was consigned. To what extent horse-drawn carts or wagons were used to supplement these pack trains at this early period can never be known, but it is fair to assume that their use was confined to the summer months. The state of the roads was then such that any heavy-laden cart would sink up to the axle in mud during the winter.

With the gradual improvement of roads that followed the setting up of local Turnpike Trusts and the use by such trusts of the improved road-making methods introduced by Macadam and Telford, horse-drawn freight vehicles slowly superseded the use of pack animals. In the South Devon ball clay industry horses and carts were in universal use for at least a hundred years to carry the clay from the pits to clay cellars beside the canal and river wharves. It was the practice to hire these from local farmers, who had doubtless furnished the earlier pack trains also. The carts were 'rented' at so much a tally. It is clear that these carts were sometimes used to supplement river barges by carrying clay to Teignmouth, although the tonnage so carried can never have been great because we are told that the Teignmouth quays were little used for clay traffic until their rebuilding by the Teignmouth Quay Company.

In 1901 the Devonshire County Council proposed to introduce a bylaw whereby carts exceeding 21cwt capacity would be compelled to fit wheels having tyres not less than 4in wide. As the typical ball clay cart carried not less than the traditional clayworker's 'ton' of

22½cwt on 3in tyres, this proposal was vigorously and successfully opposed by WBB. This little episode is of interest because it reveals two things: that the state of the local Devon roads must still have been very bad at the beginning of this century and that WBB, in common with other clay firms, still relied heavily on horse-drawn transport. By this date a considerable proportion of the clay companies' hired horse transport was used to haul clay from the workings to railway sidings instead of to canal or river wharves or harbour quays.

The South Devon Railway, which extended the broad (7ft) gauge metals from Exeter to Plymouth, was authorised in July 1844, was opened to Teignmouth in May 1846 and to Newton Abbot by the end of the same year. As is well known, the section between Exeter and Newton was the subject of Brunel's disastrous experiment with 'atmospheric' traction—the 'atmospheric caper', as it was called locally.* As mentioned in the previous chapter, early railways such as the SDR had their sights fixed on passengers and perishables and did not greatly concern themselves with such bulky, low value freights as ball clay. Therefore, apart from the effects—largely indirect—of its 1851 extension to Teignmouth old quay, the coming of the SDR appears to have had very little impact on the ball clay industry. It was not until after the Moretonhampstead & South Devon Railway was opened for traffic in July 1866 that railways began to affect clay distribution. Although the MSDR was authorised as an independent company in 1862 and not amalgamated with the SDR until a decade later, it was to all intents and purposes a broad-gauge branch of the SDR from the beginning since the latter company played a large part in its promotion and was responsible for working the line from the outset.

A new railway cutting through the heart of the Bovey basin, a railway which usurped part of the formation of the old Haytor tramway and ran parallel with the Stover canal—which it had

* On the theory that a single line using atmospheric traction could handle as much traffic as a double line using steam locomotives, the SDR was originally single throughout. It was doubled as far as Newton Abbot from Exeter in 1865.

purchased for £8,000—was something that the clay companies could not ignore. Clay loading facilities were provided at Heathfield station, then known as Chudleigh Road,* in 1874 and there was a similar provision, though upon a smaller scale, at Teigngrace Halt. In March 1890 a special siding for clay traffic was constructed at Teignbridge and a similar siding was opened in 1938 at East Golds at the request of the Newton Abbot Clay Company. As recently as 1948, by agreement with British Railways, WBB constructed a new clay loading ramp at Teignbridge at the firm's own expense. There was some objection to this move from rival clay companies, but this evaporated when WBB made it clear that the ramp could be freely used by all.

As railways became increasingly competitive and as the tonnage of South Devon clay shipped to countries outside Europe, and particularly to the New World, continued to rise, so the Moretonhampstead Branch line brought an increasing amount of clay traffic to the main line. On reaching Newton Abbot, traffic due to be shipped deep-sea might either travel eastwards and northwards to Bristol and Avonmouth, or westwards to the Cornish port of Fowey. This growth of traffic became most marked after the SDR amalgamated with the GWR in February 1876. In the same year the GWR acquired the Cornwall and West Cornwall railways, which became extensions of its main line as far as Penzance, and leased the Cornwall Minerals Railway and the Port of Fowey. The CMR had been built, and the Port of Fowey developed, in anticipation of traffic in granite, iron ore and copper ore from Fowey Consols mine. This failed to materialise and it was as a deep-water port for the export of china clay that Fowey achieved fame. In 1919

* The station's name was changed to Heathfield when the belated opening of the little Teign Valley line to Chudleigh in 1882 made it a junction. Originally a satellite of the SDR, the TVR company antagonised its sponsor by proposing to extend its line to Exeter. The SDR's reaction to this threat of competition was to refuse support to a near-bankrupt concern which, in desperation, turned for salvation to the narrow gauge London & South Western Railway with the result that it was built to the narrow gauge. Thus Heathfield was not literally a junction but one of the the smallest stations where a break of gauge occurred.

Page 143   (above) *Compressing pallets under a press;* (below) *loading pallets into container using a fork truck and a lift*

Page 144 (above) *Co-operation: C. D. Pike explains his Company's plans to Trade Unionists;* (below) *reward: C. D. Pike receiving the Queen's Award for Industry on behalf of his Company*

the GWR acquired outright ownership of the port and proceeded to modernise it by installing hydraulic wagon tipplers on three of the jetties and an electric rail-to-ship conveyor on the fourth jetty. Although small by comparison with the growth of the port's china clay trade, a certain tonnage of South Devon ball clay was rail-freighted to Fowey for shipment to the New World. This method of shipment never became popular, because, unlike china clay, ball clay was too sticky to slide from the wagons when they were tippled.

So far as traffic between the clay workings and Teignmouth is concerned, it has been said that the barge trade on the Teign estuary only survived as long as it did because the railway was not interested in such a short haul of a low-rated freight. This may have been so in the case of the SDR but it certainly was not true in GWR days. In 1909 the GWR quoted Whiteway & Co 1s 5d per ton to convey clay from Teignbridge clay siding to Teignmouth Quay. This was a highly competitive rate when we remember that the equivalent charge on the two canals as far back as 1845 was 1s 6d. However, the railways seems to have made little or no impression on this short-haul traffic, probably because the Teignmouth Quay Company had not then modernised its quays and by the time it did so both rail and canal had lost out to road transport. Another reason was that ships arriving at Teignmouth for loading often gave too short a notice for rail transport to be feasible and, even so, wagons were apt to arrive at the quayside in the wrong order.

On the traffic to the ball clay producers' principal home market, the Staffordshire Potteries, railways were able to make little impression because, as already explained, the firms there were geared to the traditional all-water route. To internal destinations elsewhere, however, rail traffic became quite considerable, so much so that in its first year of working the Newton Abbot Clay Company invested in ten private-owner wagons. Large numbers of such wagons were owned by the Cornish china clay companies, but for some reason they did not suit the ball clay trade of South Devon, perhaps because of the discharging difficulty. The precedent was

I

not taken up by any other clay company and the ten wagons were soon sold.

From the 1930s onward, road vehicles began to claim an ever larger share of ball clay transport for the home market, but in 1964 the railways made a determined bid to recapture a share of the traffic by introducing a liner train service between Cornwall, Devon and the Staffordshire Potteries. This train, which runs five days a week, begins its journey with a freight of Cornish china clay, but usually picks up additional wagons loaded with ball clay at Newton Abbot. The first of these 'clay liner' trains left Newton Abbot on 18 November 1965.

Most firms in the ball clay industry seem to have relied almost exclusively on the horse for short-haul road transport until after World War I, although it is on record that in 1913 WBB hired some 'steam carts' from Hexter, Humpherson & Co at 37s 6d per cart per day in order to clear a back-log of work which had accumulated due to the strike of that year. Although the make of these vehicles is not specified, they were almost certainly built by the Mann's Patent Steam Cart and Wagon Co Ltd of Leeds. Mann was the only steam vehicle builder to use the term 'steam cart'. The original steam cart —a small three-wheeled traction engine with a cart body over the single rear wheel—was the parent of all mechanical load-carrying road vehicles. It was originally designed and patented by P. J. Parmiter of Tisbury, Wilts in 1886 and later built by Mann and developed by that firm—and by many other makers—into what became known as the overtype steam wagon. It is likely that the machines used in South Devon were the improved version of the Mann steam cart, with a load capacity of 2 tons, which was built in fair quantity from 1905 onwards.

During World War I, in common with many another industry, most of the horses employed in the clay trade were requisitioned for military service. This insatiable military demand for horses to make good the terrible losses on the Western Front was undoubtedly an important factor in the great changeover from horses to mechanical power on the roads although it has seldom been recognised as such. Admittedly, new vehicles were not easy to obtain during the war years and, in the case of the clay industry, business was so slack that the need for road transport was very much reduced. Nevertheless, it is on record that WBB invested in its first steam wagon in 1917. Once it had lost its horses, there was naturally a tendency after the war for a firm to invest in mechanical transport, especially when new vehicles of greatly improved design, performance and reliability began to appear. So it was in the case of WBB where the single steamer originally purchased became one of a small fleet. Like the vehicles the firm had hired in 1913, these were Mann overtype wagons. WBB also owned several ex WD Dennis petrol lorries on solid tyres at this time and in 1921 W. J. V. Watts prepared a memorandum on comparative transport expenses for his board which showed that the running costs of the steamers were considerably less than those of the petrol vehicles and the latter were replaced by steamers. There is no reason to doubt the correctness of his finding for, where heavy road haulage was concerned, the petrol engine certainly had an inordinate appetite for an expensive fuel. For this reason alone steam vehicles would have held their own in this field had not the government introduced changes in vehicle taxation which placed them at a disadvantage. This was what induced WBB to get rid of its entire road steamer fleet in 1930. They were no longer economic.

After the end of World War I, the new firm of Newton Abbot Clays Ltd owned four horses and one Model T Ford lorry. Some of the firm's directors got together in 1923 and purchased a new steam wagon and trailer—make undisclosed— and formed a subsidiary company, called the Teign Valley Transport Co Ltd, to operate it. However, most of Newton Abbot Clays' road haulage was done for them under contract by the Clifford Estate and this set a precedent which was gradually adopted throughout the South Devon ball clay industry. Firms might employ their own dumper trucks or tipping lorries for internal transport between mine or open

pit and storage shed or processing plant, but where external hauls
were concerned demand fluctuated to such an extent that it soon
became obvious that it was better and cheaper to hire than to own
road vehicles. The contractor could offer a more flexible service and
avoided the under-use of costly vehicles. The industry had begun
using local road hauliers by the mid 1920s and the practice has been
continued ever since; indeed two local road haulage contractors,
Eggbeers' Transport and F. R. Cook & Son (Cook's Transport)
carried clay for the industry in the 1920s and are still carrying it
today. Newton Abbot Clays Ltd first asked George Eggbeer to
supply transport when the company got rid of its four horses.
Similarly, the forerunner of another local haulage contractor, W. L.
Vallance, was a local farmer who hired out horses and carts.

Today many haulage contractors, large and small, are engaged in
clay haulage, either to Teignmouth or to destinations further afield
and it is difficult to give an accurate estimate of the tonnage carried
by road. One local contractor alone estimates that he carried 60,000
tons of clay during the ten-year period 1953–63, since when clay
output has greatly increased. This vast expansion in the use of road
transport, as reflected in the history of this one industry, would
never have come about but for the introduction of the high-speed
diesel engine. Despite the modern tax on fuel oil, it is a vastly more
economical and reliable power unit than the petrol engine which it
replaced, and in the early 1930s it transformed the economics of
heavy road haulage almost overnight.

In recent years this intensive use of road transport created a local
'nuisance' problem in the shape of the amount of clay which was
being carried on to the roads. On the clay workings, the intricate
tread patterns of lorry tyres tended to fill up with clay which was
then flung off by centrifugal force as soon as the lorry gathered
speed on the public road. The result was becoming a menace to
other road users, particularly in wet weather when the clay tended
to spread over the road surface in a thin film. WBB's first response
to this intractable problem was to acquire an elaborate road sweeper,

but it soon became clear that the only right way of dealing with it was to prevent the clay getting on to the public road at all. This was not so easy; WBB's engineers had to modify the whole layout of works operations in such a way that all road vehicles would have to travel over a considerable length of private road before gaining the public highway. Here preliminary spillage could take place; here also there was arranged a series of cattle grids designed to flex the tyres and so dislodge embedded clay. So far as the public roads are concerned, this scheme has brought about a considerable improvement, but it has created a need for new plant to clean up the private roads!

By no means all the present clay haulage contractors are Devon based. Many come from the Midlands. For example, when a Staffordshire pottery manufacturer consigns a load of his wares by road to the West Country he usually arranges for the lorry to back-load with clay. This problem of finding return loads is one which has beset every form of transport throughout the ages. Two-way loading can transform the economics of any transport operation, and to be able to secure return loads is particularly valuable in the case of a low-rated freight such as ball clay because obviously an operator is only too glad to accept any load rather than have his vehicle, whether it be a ship, a railway wagon or a lorry, return empty. Unfortunately for the ball clay industry, however, Devon, which in the past has always been a nett importing county, now exports more than it receives. The effect of this is that there are fewer empty vehicles looking for loads and outgoing transport costs have risen accordingly.

The same problem of the return load bedevils the use of special-purpose vehicles on long hauls. For example, WBB investigated the possibility of employing road tankers which could deliver powdered clay in bulk, but had to postpone the idea until very recently owing to the difficulty of obtaining suitable return loads for such vehicles. So instead, in November 1968, the company introduced its 'Unit Pack' system for the loading and despatch of its bagged powdered clays. Each of these packs consists of forty 50lb (25kg) bags of clay securely fastened down to a standard wooden pallet with extensible nylon ties and covered with a cardboard top. The resulting unit is very economical in warehouse space and suitable for stowage in ships, containers and flat-bed road vehicles. It is also readily adapted to modern mechanical handling devices such as fork-lift trucks and the like.

By the time it has arrived at some distant destination overseas, the transport costs on a consignment of ball clay may amount to one-half, or as much as two-thirds, of the intrinsic value of the clay. Now that WBB sends its clay products to fifty-four countries from New Zealand to Iceland, the intelligent planning of the most economical form of transport and the route to be used to a particular destination becomes vital to the success of the whole export operation. For example, with the closure of the Suez Canal, delivery to a destination such as Teheran became a problem. The best solution was found to be as follows: road transport from Devon to Rochester; Rochester to Leningrad by sea; canal from Leningrad to the Caspian; then by sea again to North Iran and thence by road to Teheran. Although this route may sound tortuous and complicated, it proved to be cheaper than the alternative of consigning the clay by sea round the Cape. It is careful planning of this kind which wins Queen's Awards for exports and which has made the initials WBB known throughout the world.

Bibliography

BOOKS

Ashcroft-Hawley, V. R. G. and Mitchell, D. *Devon Ball Clays and China Clays* (Newton Abbot: Watts, Blake, Bearne & Co Ltd, 1960)

Barton, R. M. *A History of the Cornish China-Clay Industry* (Truro: D. Bradford Barton, 1966)

Bloore, W. J. and Booth, C. L. 'Potters' or Ball Clay Mining in South Devon', *The Mining Engineer*, No 11 (London: Institution of Mining Engineers, 1961)

Bulley, J. A. 'Beginnings of the Devon Ball Clay Trade', The Devonshire Assn *Proceedings*, Vol 1 (Exeter, 1862)

Clark, R. H. *The Development of the English Steam Wagon* (Norwich: Goose & Son, 1963)

De Salis, H. Rodolph. *Bradshaw's Guide to the Canals and Navigable Rivers of England and Wales* (London: Henry Blacklock, 1904)

Ewans, M. C. *The Haytor Granite Tramway and Stover Canal* (Dawlish: David & Charles, 1964; 2nd imp, revised, 1966)

Hadfield, Charles. *The Canals of South West England* (Newton Abbot: David & Charles, 1967)

MacDermot, E. T. *History of the Great Western Railway*, Vol II (London: GWR, 1931)

Mankowitz, W. *Wedgwood* (London: Batsford, 1953, rep Spring Books, 1966)

Mankowitz, W. and Haggar, R. *The Concise Encyclopaedia of English Pottery and Porcelain* (London: André Deutsch, 1957)

Pengelly, W. 'Lignite Clays of Bovey Tracey', The Devonshire Assn *Proceedings*, Vol 87 (Exeter, 1925)

Pike Bros, Fayle & Co Ltd. *The Clay Mines of Dorset* (London: Harley Publishing Co, 1960)

Roscoe, William. *Manual of the Potter* (London: Alec Tarrant, 1963)

Scott, Dr Alexander. *Ball Clays*, Geological Survey of Great Britain, Vol XXI (London: HMSO, 1929)

——. *Devon Ball Clay* (Newton Abbot: Devon & Courtenay Clay Co)

Stretton, Norman. *The Indio Pottery at Bovey Tracey*; a Lecture (London: Wellcome Institute of the History of Medicine, 1970)

Worrall, W. E. *Raw Materials* Institute of Ceramics Text Book Series (London: Maclaren, 2nd ed 1969)

UNPUBLISHED THESIS

Clark, E. A. G. *The Estuarine Ports of the Exe and the Teign* (London: University of London, 1954)

REPORTS

1892 (August). *Teignmouth Bar* by J. C. Inglis, Plymouth

1946 (March). *Report of the Enquiry on the Ball-Clay Industry* (Board of Trade) (London: HMSO)

1953 (Sept). *Ball Clay Standing Conference: Report of the Conference* (Bristol: Ministry of Housing & Local Government)

1966 (Feb). *Teignmouth Harbour Fluorescent Tracer Experiment*, Ministry of Technology (Wallingford: Hydraulics Research Station Report EX304)

1970 (Jan). *Teignmouth Harbour Model Study* (Improvements to Harbour Entrance) (Wallingford: HRS Report EX472)

1970 (April). *Teignmouth Harbour Model Study* (Possibility of maintaining a deeper channel to the quays, and the effect of a rubble-mound breakwater at the harbour entrance) (Wallingford: HRS EX489)

1971 (March). *Proposed Improvements to Teignmouth Harbour* (London: Lewis & Duvivier)

Index

Page numbers in italic indicate illustrations